W. B. SAUNDERS COMPANY • PHILADELPH

GAME THEORY

GUILLERMO OWEN
Associate Professor of Mathematics
Fordham University

ONDON • TORONTO • 1968

W. B. Saunders Company: West Washington Square
Philadelphia, Pa. 19105

12 Dyott Street
London W. C. 1

1835 Yonge Street
Toronto 7, Ontario

Game Theory

 Library of Congress catalog card number 68-10405.

PREFACE

For several years there has been a definite need for a text which covers comprehensively the salient aspects of both two-person and n-person game theory from a mathematical point of view. It is my hope that this book will fill this gap.

Broadly speaking, the first five chapters of this book form one part (two-person game theory) while the last five chapters form a second part (n-person game theory). The two parts are independent of each other and could be treated as separate one-semester courses. Similarly, an elementary course (with a theoretical orientation) could be formed by taking only Chapters I, II, VI, VIII, and IX. This could be a very pleasant one-semester offering. Generally, the instructor can make up a course of such subjects as he wishes, without too much need to cover the remaining chapters. It might be added that most texts on the subject cover the matter which appears in Chapters II, III, VIII, and IX.

I have endeavored to maintain mathematical strictness in the presentation of the material. At the same time it has been my desire, especially in the second half of the book, to give, wherever possible, a heuristic interpretation of the mathematical argument. Game theory is, after all, a mathematical description of certain sociological phenomena; it would be a poor text indeed which did not relate the mathematics to the social situation.

In choosing the material to be presented in this book, my main motivation has been the presentation of game-theoretic ideas to the upper-level undergraduate or beginning graduate student. Thus I felt that it would be best to begin the book with some problems which have been solved. This gives the student the satisfactory feeling of treating a closed question; figuratively, it gives him something to sink his teeth into. This is, indeed, the case with two-person game theory. I have avoided some parts of this theory, notably the question of information in extensive games, because it has invariably been my impression, in teaching the course, that the introduction of these concepts does nothing to facilitate the presentation of the main matter. Rather, it hinders it, and should best be left to advanced discussions of game theory. The postponement of the discussion of utility theory until the latter half of this book has a similar purpose: though it is central to the study of *n*-person games, it has proved, generally, a hindrance to the two-person zero-sum theory.

I believe that several of the topics treated here appear for the first time in a text. These include differential games, the bargaining set, and games for a continuum of players. I have treated these topics in detail, though of course leaving out many of the more complicated aspects of each. Their inclusion in this text should serve to give the student an idea of the many new directions which the study of game theory is taking.

The prerequisites for a fruitful reading of this book are, of course, some knowledge of the calculus and a small amount of elementary probability theory. Some knowledge of abstract measure theory would naturally be useful, but is by no means necessary. Finally, some familiarity with the properties of convex sets and functions is definitely necessary. Since, however, courses in this subject are not usually given in most universities, I have included the more important portions of this theory in an Appendix to the book. Similarly, the Brouwer and Kakutani fixed point theorems, which are so useful in many sections of game theory, are included without proof.

The problems have mostly been taken from the literature; they are of importance in that they give counter-examples to certain plausible conjectures, or else give outlines of the proofs of certain theorems which I did not feel could be included in their entirety. A few are elementary exercises.

I have tried to make the bibliography extensive enough so that any reader can find, at first hand, whatever details are missing from my treatment of certain topics. It is not supposed to be exhaustive; exhaustive bibliographies have been published in the past, notably in Luce and Raiffa's fine book, *Games and Decisions*, and in the *Annals of Mathematics Studies No. 40*.

I would like to thank Professor Albert Tucker of Princeton University and Professor John Isbell of Case Institute of Technology for their many helpful comments and suggestions for the improvement of the original manuscript. Several of the examples and exercises were included at their explicit suggestion. I would also like to thank Helen Gwozdz, Ellen Mooney, and Mrs. Catherine deRosa for their invaluable help in typing the manuscript. Finally, I would like to thank my wife for her encouragement and faith in me.

G. O.

VAN BOVEN, HAROLD

CONTENTS

CHAPTER VII

CHAPTER VIII

CHAPTER IX

CHAPTER X

CHAPTER I

DEFINITION OF A GAME

I.1 GENERAL NOTIONS

The general idea of a game is that with which we are familiar in the context of parlor games. Starting from a given point, there is a sequence of personal moves, at each of which one of the players chooses from among several possibilities; interspersed among these there may also be chance, or random, moves such as throwing a die or shuffling a deck of cards.

Examples of this type of game are chess, in which there are no chance moves (except for the determination of who shall play first), bridge, in which chance plays a much greater part, but in which skill is still important, and roulette, which is entirely a game of chance in which skill plays no part.

The examples of bridge and chess help to point out another important element of a game. In fact, in a chess game each player knows every move that has been made so far, while in bridge a player's knowledge is usually very imperfect. Thus, in some games, a player is unable to determine which of several possible moves has actually been made, either by an opposing player, or by chance. The practical result of this is that, when a player makes a move, he does not know the exact position of the game, and must make his move remembering that there are several possible actual positions.

Finally, at the end of a game, there is normally some payoff to the players (in the form of money, prestige or satisfaction) which depends on the progress of the game. We may think of this as a function which assigns a payoff to each "terminal position" of the game.

I.2 GAMES IN EXTENSIVE FORM

In our general idea of a game, therefore, three elements enter: (1) alternation of moves, which can be either personal or random (chance) moves, (2) a possible lack of knowledge and (3) a payoff function.

We define, first, a *topological tree* or *game tree* as a finite collection of nodes, called *vertices*, connected by lines, called *arcs*, so as to form a connected figure which includes no simple closed curves. Thus it follows that, given any two vertices A and B, there is a unique sequence of arcs and nodes joining A to B.

From this we obtain:

I.2.1 Definition. Let Γ be a topological tree with a distinguished vertex, A. We say that a vertex, C, *follows* the vertex B if the sequence of arcs joining A to C passes through B. We say C follows B *immediately* if C follows B and, moreover, there is an arc joining B to C. A vertex X is said to be *terminal* if no vertex follows X.

I.2.2 Definition. By an *n-person game in extensive form* is meant

(α) A topological tree, Γ, with a distinguished vertex A called the *starting point* of Γ.

(β) A function, called the *payoff function*, which assigns an n-vector to each terminal vertex of Γ.

(γ) A partition of the non-terminal vertices of Γ into $n + 1$ sets $S_0, S_1, \ldots, S_n$, called the *player sets*.

(δ) A probability distribution, defined at each vertex of S_0, among the immediate followers of this vertex.

(ϵ) For each $i = 1, \ldots, n$, a sub-partition of S_i into subsets S_i^j, called *information sets*, such that two vertices in the same information set have the same number of immediate followers and no vertex can follow another vertex in the same information set.

(ζ) For each information set S_i^j, an index set I_i^j, together with a 1–1 mapping of the set I_i^j onto the set of immediate followers of each vertex of S_i^j.

The elements of a game are seen here: condition α states that there is a starting point; β gives a payoff function; γ divides the moves into chance moves (S_0) and personal moves which correspond to the n players ($S_1, \ldots, S_n$); δ defines a randomization scheme at each chance move; ϵ divides a player's moves into "information sets": he knows which information set he is in, but not which vertex of the information set.

I.2.3 Example. In the game of *matching pennies* (Figure I.2.1), player 1 chooses "heads" (H) or "tails" (T). Player 2, not knowing player 1's choice, also chooses "heads" or "tails." If the two choose alike, then player 2 wins a cent from player 1; otherwise, player 1 wins a cent from 2. In the game tree shown, the vectors at the terminal vertices represent the payoff function; the numbers near the other vertices denote the player to whom the move corresponds. The shaded area encloses moves in the same information set.

I.2.4 Example. The game of pure strategy, or GOPS, is played by giving each of two players an entire suit of cards (thirteen cards). A third suit is shuffled, and the cards of this third suit are then turned up, one by one. Each time one has been turned up, each player turns up one of his cards at will: the one who turns up the larger card "wins" the third card. (If both turn up a card of the same denomination, neither wins.) This continues until the three suits are exhausted. At this point, each player totals the

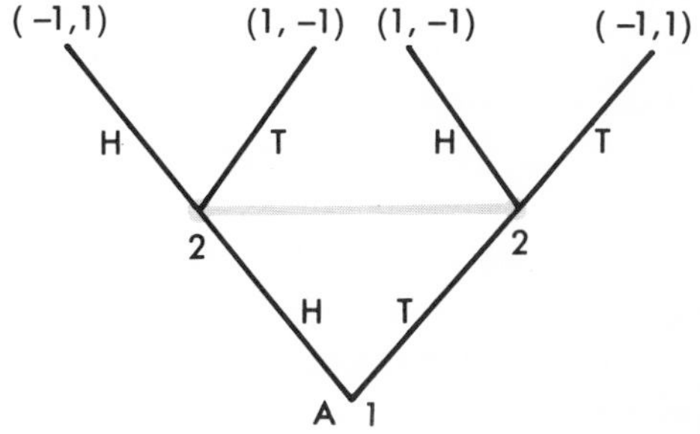

FIGURE I.2.1

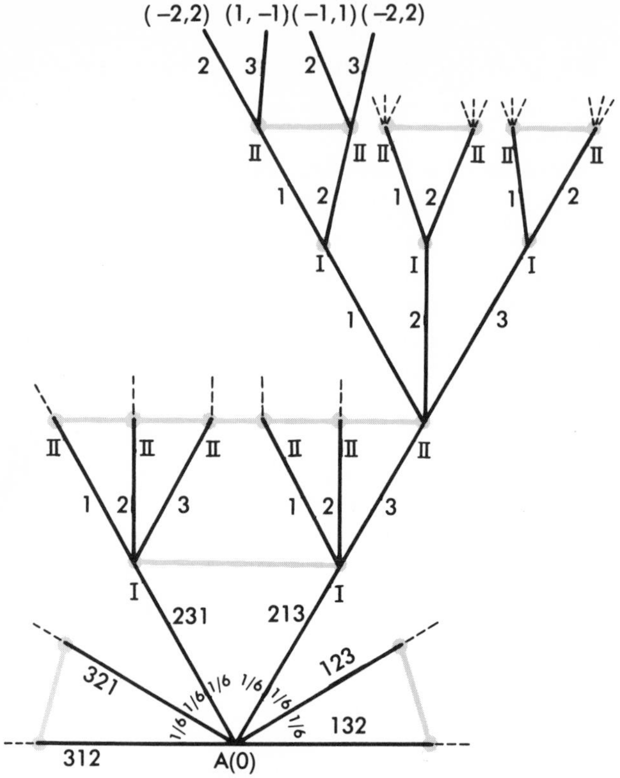

FIGURE I.2.2

number of spots on the cards he has "won"; the "score" is the difference between what the two players have.

With thirteen-card suits, this game's tree is too large to give here; however, we can give part of the tree of an analogous game using three-card suits (Figure I.2.2).

There is a single chance move, the shuffle, which orders the cards in one of the six possible ways, each having a probability of $\frac{1}{6}$. After this the moves correspond to the two players, I and II, until the game ends. We have drawn parts of the game tree, including the initial point, several branches, and four of the terminal points. The remaining branches are similar to those we have already drawn. With respect to information, we have:

I.2.5 Definition. Player I is said to have *perfect information* in Γ if his information sets S_i^j each consist of one element.

The game Γ is said to have perfect information if each player has perfect information in Γ.

For example, chess and checkers have perfect information, whereas bridge and poker do not.

I.3 STRATEGIES. THE NORMAL FORM

The intuitive meaning of a strategy is that of a plan for playing a game. We may think of a player as saying to himself, "If such and such happens, I'll act in such and such a manner." Thus we have

I.3.1 Definition. By a *strategy* for player i is meant a function which assigns, to each of player i's information sets S_i^j, one of the arcs which follows a representative vertex of S_i^j.

The set of all strategies for player i will be called Σ_i.

In general, we are accustomed to the idea that a player decides his move in a game only a few moves, at best, in advance, and quite usually only at the moment he must make it. In practice this must be so, for in a game such as chess or poker the number of possible moves is so great that no one can plan for every contingency very much in advance. From a purely theoretic point of view, however, we can overlook this practical limitation, and assume that, even before the game starts, each player has already decided what he will do in each case. Thus, we are actually assuming that each player chooses a strategy before the game starts.

Since this is so, it only remains to carry out the chance moves. Moreover, the chance moves may all be combined into a single move, whose result, together with the strategies chosen, determines the outcome of the game.

Actually, what we are interested in, and what the players are interested in, is deciding which one of the strategies is best, from the point of view of maximizing the player's share of the payoff (i.e., player i will want to maximize the ith component of the payoff function). As, however, no one knows, except probabilistically, what the results of the chance moves will be, it becomes natural to take the mathematical expectation of the payoff function, given that the players are using a given n-tuple of strategies. Therefore we shall use the notation

$$\pi(\sigma_1, \sigma_2, \ldots, \sigma_n) =$$
$$(\pi_1(\sigma_1, \ldots, \sigma_n), \pi_2(\ldots), \ldots, \pi_n(\sigma_1, \ldots, \sigma_n))$$

to represent the mathematical expectation of the payoff function, given that player i is using strategy $\sigma_i \in \Sigma_i$.

From this, it becomes possible to tabulate the function $\pi(\sigma_1, \ldots, \sigma_n)$ for all possible values of $\sigma_1, \ldots, \sigma_n$, either in the form of a relation, or by setting up an n-dimensional array of n-vectors. (In case $n = 2$, this reduces to a matrix whose elements are pairs of real numbers.) This n-dimensional array is called the *normal form* of the game Γ.

I.3.2 Example. In the game of matching pennies (see Example I.2.3) each player has the two strategies, "heads" and "tails." The normal form of this game is the matrix

	H	T
H	$(-1, 1)$	$(1, -1)$
T	$(1, -1)$	$(-1, 1)$

(where each row represents a strategy of player I, and each column a strategy of player II).

I.3.3 Example. Consider the following game: An integer z is chosen at random, with possible values 1, 2, 3, 4 (each with probability $\frac{1}{4}$). Player I, without knowing the results of this move, chooses an integer x. Player II, knowing neither the result of the chance move nor I's choice, chooses an integer y. The payoff is

$$(|y - z| - |x - z|, |x - z| - |y - z|)$$

i.e., the point is to guess close to z.

In this game each player has four strategies: 1, 2, 3, 4, since other integers are of little use. If, for instance, I chooses 1 and II chooses 3, then the payoff will be $(2, -2)$ with probability $\frac{1}{4}$, $(0, 0)$ with probability $\frac{1}{4}$, and $(-2, 2)$ with probability $\frac{1}{2}$. The expected payoff, then, is $\pi(1, 3) = (-\frac{1}{2}, \frac{1}{2})$. Calculating all the values of $\pi(\sigma_1, \sigma_2)$, we obtain

	1	2	3	4
1	$(0, 0)$	$(-\frac{1}{2}, \frac{1}{2})$	$(-\frac{1}{2}, \frac{1}{2})$	$(0, 0)$
2	$(\frac{1}{2}, -\frac{1}{2})$	$(0, 0)$	$(0, 0)$	$(\frac{1}{2}, -\frac{1}{2})$
3	$(\frac{1}{2}, -\frac{1}{2})$	$(0, 0)$	$(0, 0)$	$(\frac{1}{2}, -\frac{1}{2})$
4	$(0, 0)$	$(-\frac{1}{2}, \frac{1}{2})$	$(-\frac{1}{2}, \frac{1}{2})$	$(0, 0)$

expected payoffs

I.3.4 Definition. A game is said to be finite if its tree contains only finitely many vertices.

Under this definition, most of our parlor games are finite. Chess, for instance, is finite, thanks to the laws which end the game after certain sequences of moves.

It should be seen that, in a finite game, each player has only a finite number of strategies.

I.4 EQUILIBRIUM *n*-TUPLES

I.4.1 Definition. Given a game Γ, a strategy n-tuple $(\sigma_1^*, \sigma_2^*, \ldots, \sigma_n^*)$ is said to be *in equilibrium*, or an *equilibrium n-tuple* if and only if, for any $i = 1, \ldots, n$, and any $\hat{\sigma}_i \in \Sigma_i$,

$$\pi_i(\sigma_1^*, \ldots, \sigma_{i-1}^*, \hat{\sigma}_i, \sigma_{i+1}^*, \ldots, \sigma_n^*) \leq \pi_i(\sigma_1^*, \ldots, \sigma_n^*).$$

In other words, an n-tuple of strategies is said to be in equilibrium if no player has any positive reason for changing his strategy, assuming that none of the other players is going to change strategies. If, in such a case, each player knows what the others will play, then he has reason to play the strategy which will give such an equilibrium n-tuple, and the game becomes very stable.

I.4.2 Example. In the game with normal form:

	β_1	β_2
α_1	$(2, 1)$	$(0, 0)$
α_2	$(0, 0)$	$(1, 2)$

both (α_1, β_1) and (α_2, β_2) are equilibrium pairs.

Unfortunately, not every game has equilibrium n-tuples. As an example, the game of matching pennies (Example I.3.2) has no equilibrium pairs.

In general, if a game has no equilibrium n-tuples, we usually see the several players trying to outguess each other, keeping their strategies secret. This suggests (and it is indeed true) that in games of perfect information, equilibrium n-tuples exist.

To prove this statement, we must study the question of decomposition of a game.

A game Γ will be said to decompose at a vertex X if there are no information sets which include vertices from both of: (a) X, and all its followers, and (b) the remainder of the game tree. In this case, we can distinguish the subgame, Γ_X, consisting of X, and all its followers, and the quotient game, Γ/X, which consists of all the remaining vertices, plus X. For the quotient game, X will be a terminal vertex; the payoff here can be considered to be Γ_X: i.e., the payoff at this vertex is a play of the subgame Γ_X.

Now, as we have seen, a strategy for i is a function whose domain consists of the information sets of player I. If we decompose a game at X, then we can also decompose the strategy σ into two parts: $\sigma_{|\Gamma/X}$, obtained by restricting σ to information sets in Γ/X, and $\sigma_{|\Gamma_X}$, obtained by restricting σ to Γ_X. Conversely, a strategy for Γ/X and a strategy for Γ_X can be combined in the obvious way to yield a strategy for the larger game Γ.

I.4.3 Theorem. Let Γ decompose at X. For $\sigma_i \in \Sigma_i$, assign to X (considered as a terminal vertex of Γ/X) the payoff

$$\pi_X(\sigma_{1|\Gamma_X}, \sigma_{2|\Gamma_X}, \ldots, \sigma_{n|\Gamma_X}).$$

In this case,

$$\pi(\sigma_1, \ldots, \sigma_n) = \pi_{\Gamma/X}(\sigma_{1|\Gamma/X}, \ldots, \sigma_{n|\Gamma/X}).$$

The proof of this theorem is clear and can be left as an exercise to the reader. Briefly, it is only necessary to verify that, for each possible outcome of the chance moves, the same terminal vertex is eventually reached either in the original or in the decomposed game.

With this, we can prove:

I.4.4 Theorem. Let Γ decompose at X, and let $\sigma_i \in \Sigma_i$ be such that (a) $(\sigma_{1|\Gamma_X}, \ldots, \sigma_{n|\Gamma_X})$ is an equilibrium n-tuple for Γ_X, and (b) $(\sigma_{1|\Gamma/X}, \ldots, \sigma_{n|\Gamma/X})$ is an equilibrium n-tuple for Γ/X, with the payoff $\pi(\sigma_{1|\Gamma_X}, \ldots, \sigma_{n|\Gamma_X})$ assigned to the terminal vector X. Then $(\sigma_1, \ldots, \sigma_n)$ is an equilibrium n-tuple for Γ.

PROOF: Let $\hat{\sigma}_i \in \Sigma_i$. Because $(\sigma_{1|\Gamma_X}, \ldots, \sigma_{n|\Gamma_X})$ is an equilibrium n-tuple for Γ_X, it follows that:

$$\pi_i(\sigma_{1|\Gamma_X}, \ldots, \hat{\sigma}_{i|\Gamma_X}, \ldots, \sigma_{n|\Gamma_X}) \leq \pi_i(\sigma_{1|\Gamma_X}, \ldots, \sigma_{n|\Gamma_X}).$$

On the other hand, by (b) we know that, if we assign the payoff $\pi(\sigma_{1|\Gamma_X}, \ldots, \sigma_{n|\Gamma_X})$ to the vector X, then

$$\pi_i(\sigma_{1|\Gamma/X}, \ldots, \hat{\sigma}_{i|\Gamma/X}, \ldots, \sigma_{n|\Gamma/X}) \leq \pi_i(\sigma_{1|\Gamma/X}, \ldots, \sigma_{n|\Gamma/X}).$$

Now, the payoff (for a given set of strategies) is a weighted average of the payoffs at some of the terminal vertices of a tree. Hence, if the payoff to player i at a given terminal vertex (X, in this case) is decreased, his expected payoff, for any choice of strategies, will either remain equal or be decreased. Thus, applying Theorem I.4.3, we find that:

$$\pi_i(\sigma_1, \ldots, \hat{\sigma}_i, \ldots, \sigma_n) \leq \pi_i(\sigma_1, \ldots, \sigma_n)$$

and so $(\sigma_1, \ldots, \sigma_n)$ is an equilibrium n-tuple.

This is all we need to prove:

I.4.5 Theorem. Every finite n-person game with complete information has an equilibrium n-tuple of strategies.

PROOF: We shall define the length of a game as the largest possible number of edges that can be passed before reaching a terminal vertex, i.e., the largest possible number of moves before the game ends. Clearly a finite game has finite length. The proof is by induction on the length of the game.

If Γ has length 0, the theorem is trivially true. If it has length 1, then at most one player gets to move, and he obtains equilibrium by choosing his best alternative. If Γ has length m, then it decomposes (having complete information) into several subgames of length less than m. By the induction hypothesis, each of these subgames has an equilibrium n-tuple; by Theorem I.4.4 these form an equilibrium n-tuple for Γ.

PROBLEMS

1. An infinite game, even with perfect information, need not have an equilibrium n-tuple.
   (a) Consider a two-person game in which the two players alternate, and, at each move, each player chooses one of the two digits 0 and 1. If the digit x_i is chosen at the ith move, then each play of the game corresponds to a number

$$x = \sum_{i=1}^{\infty} x_i 2^{-i}$$

   in the interval [0, 1]. Then, player I wins one unit from player II if $x \in S$, and loses one unit if $x \notin S$, where S is some subset of [0, 1].
   (b) Each player has exactly $2^{\aleph_0}$ strategies, which can therefore be indexed σ_β, τ_β respectively for $\beta < \alpha$, where α is the smallest ordinal preceded by at least $2^{\aleph_0}$ ordinals.
   (c) Let $\langle\sigma, \tau\rangle$ denote the play (or number x) obtained if the players choose strategies σ and τ respectively. For each strategy σ of I, player II has $2^{\aleph_0}$ strategies τ which will

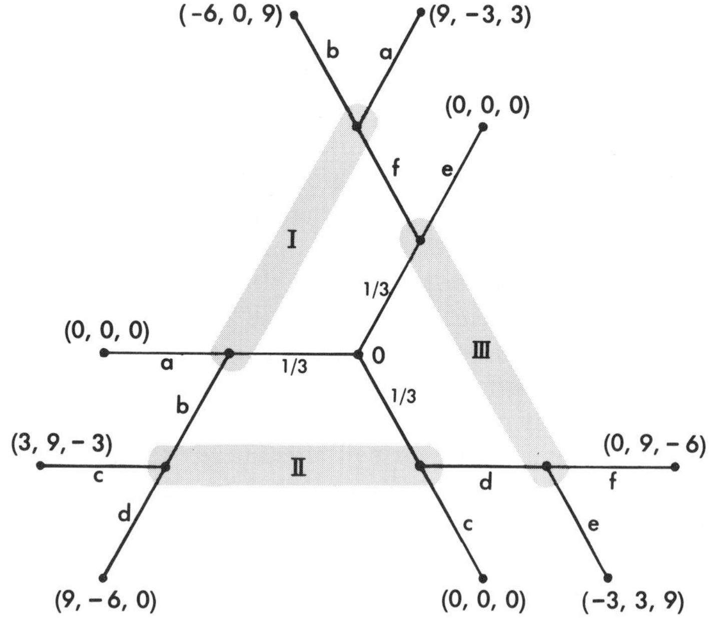

FIGURE I.p.1

give different values of $\langle \sigma, \tau \rangle$ (and similarly for each strategy τ of II).

(d) A set S can be constructed (using the axiom of choice) such that, for each σ_β, there is a τ_β with $\langle \sigma_\beta, \tau_\beta \rangle \notin S$, but for each τ_γ there is a σ_γ with $\langle \sigma_\gamma, \tau_\gamma \rangle \in S$.

2. Construct the normal form for the game whose tree is given in Figure I.p.1. The game starts at the vertex 0 (a random move); each of three players has one information set containing two vertices, with two alternatives (indexed a and b, c and d, e and f, respectively) at each vertex.

CHAPTER II

TWO-PERSON ZERO-SUM GAMES

II.1 ZERO-SUM GAMES

II.1.1 Definition. A game Γ is said to be *zero-sum* if and only if, at each terminal vertex, the payoff function $(p_1, \ldots, p_n)$ satisfies

$$2.1.1 \quad \sum_{i=1}^{n} p_i = 0.$$

In general, a zero-sum game represents a closed system: everything that someone wins must be lost by someone else. Most parlor games are of the zero-sum type. Two-person zero-sum games are sometimes called strictly competitive games.

Because of condition 2.1.1, the nth component of a payoff vector is determined by the remaining $n - 1$ components. In the case of a two-person zero-sum game, we can simply give the first component of the payoff vector; the second component is necessarily the negative of the first. In this case, we call the first component simply the *payoff*, and it is understood that the second player gives this amount to the first player.

It will be seen that a two-person zero-sum game differs from other games in that there is no reason for any negotiation between the players: in fact, whoever wins, the other loses. The meaningfulness of this will be seen from:

II.1.2 Theorem. In a two-person zero-sum game, let (σ_1, σ_2) and (τ_1, τ_2) be two equilibrium pairs. Then

(i) (σ_1, τ_2) and (τ_1, σ_2) are also equilibrium pairs, and

2.1.2 (ii) $\pi(\sigma_1, \sigma_2) = \pi(\tau_1, \tau_2) = \pi(\sigma_1, \tau_2) = \pi(\tau_1, \sigma_2)$.

PROOF: (σ_1, σ_2) is in equilibrium. Hence:

$$\pi(\sigma_1, \sigma_2) \geq \pi(\tau_1, \sigma_2).$$

On the other hand, (τ_1, τ_2) is in equilibrium. Therefore:

$$\pi(\tau_1, \sigma_2) \leq \pi(\tau_1, \tau_2).$$

Thus,

$$\pi(\sigma_1, \sigma_2) \leq \pi(\tau_1, \sigma_2) \leq \pi(\tau_1, \tau_2).$$

But, similarly,

$$\pi(\tau_1, \tau_2) \leq \pi(\sigma_1, \tau_2) \leq \pi(\sigma_1, \sigma_2)$$

and these two sets of inequalities prove 2.1.2. Now, for any $\hat{\sigma}_1$,

$$\pi(\hat{\sigma}_1, \sigma_2) \leq \pi(\sigma_1, \sigma_2) = \pi(\tau_1, \sigma_2)$$

and, for any $\hat{\sigma}_2$,

$$\pi(\tau_1, \hat{\sigma}_2) \geq \pi(\tau_1, \tau_2) = \pi(\tau_1, \sigma_2).$$

Thus (τ_1, σ_2) is in equilibrium; similarly, (σ_1, τ_2) is in equilibrium.

This theorem is not true for other games: in the game of Example I.4.2, for instance, (α_1, β_1) and (α_2, β_2) are equilibrium pairs, but the payoffs are different, and, moreover, neither (α_1, β_2) nor (α_2, β_1) is an equilibrium pair.

II.2 THE NORMAL FORM

As we have seen, the normal form of a finite zero-sum two-person game reduces to a matrix, A, with as many rows as player I has strategies and as many columns as player II has strategies. The expected payoff, assuming I chooses his i^{th} strategy and II chooses his j^{th} strategy, is the element a_{ij} in the ith row and j^{th} column of the matrix.

It will be clear that a strategy pair will be in equilibrium if, and only if, the element a_{ij} corresponding to it is both the largest in its column and the smallest in its row. Such an element, if it exists, is called a *saddle point* (by analogy with the surface of a saddle, which curves upward in one direction and downward in the other direction).

II.2.1 Example. The game matrix

$$\begin{pmatrix} 5 & 1 & 3 \\ 3 & 2 & 4 \\ -3 & 0 & 1 \end{pmatrix}$$

has a saddle point in the second row and second column.

II.2.2 Example. The game matrix

$$\begin{pmatrix} -1 & 1 \\ 1 & -1 \end{pmatrix}$$

has no saddle points.

Let us suppose that two players are actually engaged in a matrix game. In choosing strategies, player I chooses, in effect, a row, i, while player II chooses a column, j. The payoff will be the entry a_{ij}. As this is an amount which I receives from II, it is clear that player I will be trying to maximize a_{ij}, while II will be trying to minimize it. Unfortunately, neither knows for certain what his opponent's strategy will be, and this knowledge is usually of importance in deciding what strategy to use.

For instance, in the game of matching pennies (see Example I.3.2), we may picture player I as thinking: "People usually choose heads; hence II will expect me to choose heads and choose heads himself, and so I should choose tails. But perhaps II is reasoning along the same line: he'll expect me to choose tails, and so I'd better choose heads. But perhaps that is II's reasoning, so . . . ." In this case, player I could never reach a decision in which he could feel confident, and the outcome would be uncertain.

Suppose, however, that we consider the game of Example II.2.1 above. In this case, player I would probably decide to play either his first or his second strategy, and we might hear him reasoning in this manner: "I should use either my first or my second strategy, but if II figures this, he will use his second strategy, so I had better use my second strategy." Even if II guesses I's strategy, I still does well to stick to it! Thus there is a tremendous difference between these two games. In one, secrecy is important; in the other, there is no point to it. The reason, of course, is that the second game has a saddle point.

II.3 MIXED STRATEGIES

The preceding analysis, though it tells us how to play matrix games with saddle points, does not shed any light on a player's best choice for the vast majority of games, which contain no saddle points.

Let us suppose, now, that we are playing a game without saddle points, such as

$$\begin{pmatrix} 4 & 2 \\ 1 & 3 \end{pmatrix}.$$

We cannot tell what will happen. However, let us suppose that our opponent is not only unpredictable, but omniscient: he will guess correctly whatever we decide. In this case, if we are player I, we will certainly use our first strategy, with which we cannot win less than two units, whereas with our other strategy we will win only one unit. This certain win of at least two units is our "gain-floor" and we shall denote it by v'_{I}:

2.2.1 $v'_{\mathrm{I}} = \max_i \{\min_j a_{ij}\}.$

If we were player II, we should choose, under the same conditions, our second strategy, which would give us a "loss-ceiling" of three units. This loss-ceiling will be denoted by v'_{II}:

2.2.2 $v'_{\mathrm{II}} = \min_j \{\max_i a_{ij}\}.$

Thus, for matrix games, we have the idea of a gain-floor and a loss-ceiling. It would be absurd to expect I's gain-floor to exceed II's loss-ceiling. In fact, we can easily prove:

2.2.3 $v'_{\mathrm{I}} \leq v'_{\mathrm{II}}.$

The proof of this is elementary and may be left to the reader. If equality holds in 2.2.3, we have a saddle point; if not, we have a game without saddle points. For such a game, we are not certain what will happen, but we can make one statement: *player* I *should not win less than* v_I'; *player* II *should not lose more than* v_{II}'.

In a game without saddle points, if we allow the opponent to know our strategy, the best we can hope for is the "gain-floor," v_I', or the "loss-ceiling," v_{II}', depending on whether we are player I or II. If we hope to do better, it must be by refusing to let our opponent know our strategy.

This is difficult to do if we choose our strategy rationally, since there is nothing to keep our opponent from reconstructing our reasoning. We seem to be saying that we should choose our strategy irrationally. But in that case what good is all our analysis?

The answer is that the strategy should be chosen at random—hence irrationally—but the randomization scheme should be chosen rationally. This is the idea behind mixed strategies.

II.3.1 Definition. A *mixed strategy* for a player is a probability distribution on the set of his pure strategies.

In case the player has only a finite number, m, of pure strategies, a mixed strategy reduces to an m-vector, $x = (x_1, \ldots, x_m)$, satisfying

2.3.1 $$x_i \geq 0$$

2.3.2 $$\sum_{i=1}^{m} x_i = 1.$$

We shall use X to denote the set of all mixed strategies for player I, and let Y represent the set of player II's mixed strategies.

Let us suppose that players I and II are playing the matrix game A. If I chooses the mixed strategy x, and II chooses y, then the *expected payoff* will be

2.3.3 $$A(x, y) = \sum_{i=1}^{m} \sum_{j=1}^{n} x_i a_{ij} y_j$$

or, in matrix notation,

2.3.4 $$A(x, y) = xAy^T.$$

As before, player I must fear that II will discover his choice of a strategy. If this should happen, then II will certainly choose y so as to minimize $A(x, y)$; i.e., I's expected gain-floor, assuming he uses x, will be:

2.3.5 $$v(x) = \min_{y \in Y} xAy^T.$$

Now, xAy^T can be thought of as a weighted average of the expected payoffs for I if he uses x against II's pure strategies. Thus the minimum will be attained by a pure strategy, j:

2.3.6 $$v(x) = \min xA_{\cdot j}$$

(where $A_{\cdot j}$ is the jth column of the matrix A).

Hence player I should choose x so as to maximize $v(x)$, i.e., so as to obtain:

2.3.7 $$v_{\mathrm{I}} = \max_{x \in X} \min_{j} xA_{\cdot j}.$$

(One should prove that a maximum exists; however, since X is compact and the function $v(x)$ is continuous, there is no problem.) Such an x is I's *maximin* strategy.

Similarly, if II chooses y he will obtain the expected loss-ceiling

2.3.8 $$v(y) = \max_{i} A_{i\cdot} y^T$$

(where A_i is the ith row of A) and he should choose y so as to obtain:

2.3.9 $$v_{\mathrm{II}} = \min_{y \in Y} \max_{i} A_{i\cdot} y^T.$$

Such a y is II's *minimax* strategy.

Thus we obtain the two numbers v_{I} and v_{II}. These numbers are called the *values* of the game to I and II, respectively.

II.4 THE MINIMAX THEOREM

It is easily proved that, for any function $F(x, y)$ defined on any cartesian product $X \times Y$,

2.4.1 $$\max_{x \in X} \min_{y \in Y} F(x, y) \leq \min_{y \in Y} \max_{x \in X} F(x, y).$$

Hence we have:

$$v_{\mathrm{I}} \leq v_{\mathrm{II}}.$$

This is analogous to 2.2.3, and indeed, in this case as before, it is only natural that I's gain-floor cannot exceed II's loss-ceiling.

In the previous case, however, we saw that equality only held in exceptional cases. In this case, we shall actually prove:

II.4.1 Theorem (The Minimax Theorem).

$$v_{\mathrm{I}} = v_{\mathrm{II}}.$$

This theorem, the most important of game theory, has been proved in many ways. Here we shall give the proof that was given by von Neumann and Morgenstern. We start with two lemmata:

II.4.2 Lemma (Theorem of the Supporting Hyperplane). Let B be a closed convex set of points in n-dimensional Euclidean space, and let $x = (x_1, \ldots, x_n)$ be a point not in B. Then there exist numbers $p_1, \ldots, p_n, p_{n+1}$ such that

$$\sum_{i=1}^{n} p_i x_i = p_{n+1} \tag{2.4.2}$$

and

$$\sum_{i=1}^{n} p_i y_i > p_{n+1}, \quad \text{for all } y \in B. \tag{2.4.3}$$

(Geometrically, this means that we can pass a hyperplane through x such that B lies entirely "above" the hyperplane.)

PROOF: Let z be that point in B whose distance from x is a minimum. (Such a point exists because B is closed.) Now, let

$$p_i = z_i - x_i \qquad i = 1, \ldots, n$$

$$p_{n+1} = \sum_{i=1}^{n} z_i x_i - \sum_{i=1}^{n} x_i^2.$$

Clearly, 2.4.2 holds. We must show 2.4.3 also holds. Now

$$\sum_{i=1}^{n} p_i z_i = \sum_{i=1}^{n} z_i^2 - \sum_{i=1}^{n} z_i x_i$$

and hence

$$\sum p_i z_i - p_{n+1} = \sum_{i=1}^{n} z_i^2 - 2\sum_{i=1}^{n} z_i x_i + \sum_{i=1}^{n} x_i^2$$

$$= \sum_{i=1}^{n} (z_i - x_i)^2 > 0$$

Therefore

$$\sum p_i z_i > p_{n+1}.$$

Suppose now that there exists $y \in B$, such that

$$\sum_{i=1}^{n} p_i y_i \leq p_{n+1}.$$

Because B is convex, the line joining y to z must be entirely contained in B, i.e., for all $0 \leq r \leq 1$, $w_r = ry + (1 - r)z \in B$. Now the square of the distance from x to w_r is given by

$$\rho^2(x, w_r) = \sum_{i=1}^{n} (x_i - ry_i - (1 - r)z_i)^2.$$

Therefore

$$\begin{aligned} \frac{\partial \rho^2}{\partial r} &= 2 \sum_{i=1}^{n} (z_i - y_i)(x_i - ry_i - (1 - r)z_i) \\ &= 2 \sum (z_i - x_i)y_i - 2 \sum (z_i - x_i)z_i + 2 \sum r(z_i - y_i)^2 \\ &= 2 \sum p_i y_i - 2 \sum p_i z_i + 2r \sum (z_i - y_i)^2. \end{aligned}$$

If we evaluate this at $r = 0$ (i.e., $w_r = z$),

$$\left.\frac{\partial \rho^2}{\partial r}\right|_{r=0} = 2 \sum p_i y_i - 2 \sum p_i z_i.$$

But the first term on the right is assumed less than or equal to $2p_{n+1}$ while the second is greater than $2p_{n+1}$. Thus,

$$\left.\frac{\partial \rho^2}{\partial r}\right|_{r=0} < 0.$$

It follows that, for r close enough to zero,

$$\rho(x, w_r) < \rho(x, z).$$

But this contradicts the manner in which z was chosen. Therefore, for all $y \in B$, 2.4.3 must hold.

II.4.3 Lemma (Theorem of the Alternative for Matrices). Let $A = (a_{ij})$ be an $m \times n$ matrix. Then *either* (i) *or* (ii), below, must hold:

(i) The point 0 (in n-space) is contained in the convex hull of the $m + n$ points

$$\begin{aligned} a_1 &= (a_{11}, \ldots, a_{m1}) \\ &\cdots\cdots\cdots \\ a_n &= (a_{1n}, \ldots, a_{mn}) \end{aligned}$$

and

$$e_1 = (1, 0, \ldots, 0)$$
$$e_2 = (0, 1, 0, \ldots, 0)$$
$$\cdots\cdots\cdots\cdots$$
$$e_m = (0, 0, \ldots, 1)$$

(ii) There exist numbers, $x_1, \ldots, x_m$, satisfying

$$x_i > 0$$

$$\sum_{i=1}^{m} x_i = 1$$

$$\sum_{i=1}^{m} a_{ij}x_i > 0 \quad \text{for } j = 1, \ldots, n.$$

PROOF: Suppose (i) does not hold. If we apply Lemma II.4.2, there exist numbers $p_1, \ldots, p_{m+1}$ such that

$$\sum_{j=1}^{n} 0 \cdot p_j = p_{n+1}$$

(this means, of course, that $p_{n+1} = 0$) and

$$\sum_{j=1}^{n} p_j y_j > 0$$

for all y in the convex set. In particular, this will hold if y is one of the $m + n$ vectors a_i, e_j. Therefore

$$\sum a_{ij}p_i > 0 \quad \text{for all } j$$
$$p_i > 0 \quad \text{for all } i.$$

As $p_i > 0$, it follows that $\Sigma\, p_i > 0$, and we can let

$$x_i = \frac{p_i}{\sum p_i}.$$

Hence

$$\sum a_{ij}x_i > 0$$
$$x_i > 0$$
$$\sum x_i = 1.$$

With these two lemmata, we are able to prove our theorem:

PROOF OF MINIMAX THEOREM: Let A be a matrix game. By Lemma II.4.3, either (i) or (ii), above, must hold.

If (i) holds, 0 is a convex linear combination of the $m + n$

vectors. Thus, there exist $s_1, \ldots, s_{m+n}$ such that

$$\sum_{j=1}^{n} s_j a_{ij} + s_{n+i} = 0, \qquad i = 1, \ldots, m$$

$$s_j \geq 0 \qquad j = 1, \ldots, m + n$$

$$\sum_{j=i}^{m+n} s_j = 1.$$

Now, if all the numbers $s_1, \ldots, s_n$ were equal to zero, it would follow that 0 would be a convex linear combination of the m unit vectors $e_1, \ldots, e_m$, which is obviously not possible as these are independent vectors. Hence at least one of $s_1, \ldots, s_n$ is positive, and $\sum_{j=1}^{n} s_j > 0$. We can then write

$$y_j = \frac{s_j}{\sum_{j=1}^{n} s_j}$$

and we have

$$y_j \geq 0$$

$$\sum_{j=1}^{n} y_j = 1$$

$$\sum_{j=1}^{n} a_{ij} y_j = \frac{-s_{n+i}}{\sum_{j=1}^{n} s_j} \leq 0 \quad \text{for all } i.$$

Thus $v(y) \leq 0$, and $v_{\mathrm{II}} \leq 0$.

Suppose, instead, that (ii) holds. Then $v(x) > 0$, and so $v_{\mathrm{I}} > 0$.

We know therefore that it is not possible to have $v_{\mathrm{I}} \leq 0 < v_{\mathrm{II}}$. Let us suppose that we change the game A: we replace it by $B = (b_{ij})$, where

$$b_{ij} = a_{ij} + k.$$

It should be clear that for any x, y,

$$xBy^T = xAy^T + k.$$

Hence,

$$v_{\mathrm{I}}(B) = v_{\mathrm{I}}(A) + k$$

$$v_{\mathrm{II}}(B) = v_{\mathrm{II}}(A) + k.$$

As it is not possible that

$$v_{\mathrm{I}}(B) < 0 < v_{\mathrm{II}}(B),$$

it is also not possible that

$$v_{\mathrm{I}}(A) < -k < v_{\mathrm{II}}(A).$$

But k was arbitrary. Thus we cannot have $v_{\mathrm{I}} < v_{\mathrm{II}}$. But we have already seen that $v_{\mathrm{I}} \leq v_{\mathrm{II}}$. Therefore

$$v_{\mathrm{I}} = v_{\mathrm{II}}.$$

Q.E.D.

Thus, if we deal with mixed strategies, we find that I's gain-floor is precisely equal to II's loss-ceiling. The common value, v, of these two numbers is called the *value* of the game. We see that a strategy x which satisfies

2.4.4 $$\sum_{i=1}^{m} x_i a_{ij} \geq v \qquad j = 1, \ldots, n$$

is *optimal* for the first player, in the sense that there is no strategy which will give him a higher expectation than v against every strategy of II. Conversely, if y satisfies

2.4.5 $$\sum_{j=1}^{n} a_{ij} y_j \leq v \qquad i = 1, \ldots, m$$

then y is *optimal* for the second player in the same sense. Now, clearly,

$$xAy^T = v$$

for, if the right side in this equation were smaller, this would contradict II.5.2; if it were larger, this would contradict II.5.1. Hence x and y, besides being optimal, are also optimal against each other and against any other optimal strategies. We shall call any pair of optimal strategies, (x, y), a *solution* to the game.

The following theorem (a somewhat stronger form of the minimax theorem) will be useful later:

II.4.4 Theorem. In an $m \times n$ matrix game A, either player II has an optimal strategy y with $y_n > 0$, or player I has an optimal strategy x with

$$\sum_{i=1}^{m} a_{in} x_i > v.$$

To prove II.4.4, we give first the definition:

II.4.5 Definition. Let $r^k = (r_1^k, \ldots, r_n^k)$, $k = 1, \ldots, p$, be p n-vectors. Then by the *convex cone* generated by $r^1, \ldots, r^p$, we mean the set of all vectors x such that

$$x = \sum_{k=1}^{p} \lambda_k r^k$$

for some non-negative $\lambda_1, \ldots, \lambda_k$.

It is easily checked that such a cone is indeed convex.

II.4.6 Lemma (Farkas). Suppose $r^k = (r_1^k, \ldots, r_n^k)$, $k = 1, \ldots, p + 1$, are n-vectors such that any $(q_1, \ldots, q_n)$ satisfying

$$\text{2.4.6} \quad \sum_{j=1}^{n} q_j r_j^k \geq 0 \qquad k = 1, \ldots, p$$

will also satisfy

$$\text{2.4.7} \quad \sum_{j=1}^{n} q_j r_j^{p+1} \geq 0.$$

Then r^{p+1} is in the convex cone, C, generated by $r^1, \ldots, r^p$.

PROOF: Suppose $r^{p+1} \notin C$. By Lemma II.4.2, there exist numbers $q_1, \ldots, q_{n+1}$ such that

$$\sum_{j=1}^{n} q_j r_j^{p+1} = q_{n+1}$$

and

$$\sum_{j=1}^{n} q_j s_j > q_{n+1} \quad \text{for all } s \in C.$$

Now, $0 \in C$, hence $q_{n+1} < 0$. Suppose, moreover, that $\sum_{j=1}^{n} q_j s_j$ were negative for any $s \in C$. For any positive number α, $\alpha s \in C$. But by making α large enough, the form $\sum q_j \alpha s_j = \alpha \sum q_j s_j$ can be made smaller than q_{n+1}. It follows, then, that

$$\sum_{j=1}^{n} q_j r_j^{p+1} < 0$$

but

$$\sum_{j=1}^{n} q_j s_j \geq 0 \quad \text{for all } s \in C,$$

and in particular for $r = r^1, \ldots, r^p$. Hence if the conclusion of II.4.6 is false, so is its hypothesis.

Let us now proceed to prove II.4.4. Assume first that

$v(A) = 0$. Consider the $m + n$ m-vectors

$$\begin{aligned} e_1 &= (1, 0, \ldots, 0) \\ e_2 &= (0, 1, \ldots, 0) \\ &\cdots\cdots\cdots \\ e_m &= (0, 0, \ldots, 1) \\ a_1 &= (a_{11}, a_{21}, \ldots, a_{m1}) \\ &\cdots\cdots\cdots\cdots\cdots \\ a_{n-1} &= (a_{1,n-1}, a_{2,n-1}, \ldots, a_{m,n-1}) \\ -a_n &= (-a_{1n}, -a_{2n}, \ldots, -a_{mn}). \end{aligned}$$

Either $-a_n$ is in the convex cone C generated by the other $m + n - 1$ points, or it is not. Suppose $-a_n \in C$. Then there exist non-negative numbers $\mu_1, \ldots, \mu_m, \lambda_1, \ldots, \lambda_{n-1}$ such that

$$-a_{in} = \sum_{j=1}^{m} \mu_j e_{ij} + \sum_{j=1}^{n-1} \lambda_j a_{ij} \quad \text{for all } i$$

and this means

$$\sum_{j=1}^{n-1} \lambda_j a_{ij} + a_{in} = -\mu_i \leq 0 \quad \text{for all } i.$$

We now set

$$y_j = \frac{\lambda_j}{1 + \sum \lambda_i} \qquad j = 1, \ldots, n-1$$

$$y_n = \frac{1}{1 + \sum \lambda_i}.$$

It is clear that $y = (y_1, \ldots, y_n)$ is an optimal strategy for II such that $y_n > 0$.

Suppose, on the other hand, $-a_n \notin C$. There exist numbers $q_1, \ldots, q_m$ such that

2.4.8 $$\sum_{i=1}^{m} q_i e_{ij} \geq 0 \quad \text{for all } j = 1, \ldots, m$$

2.4.9 $$\sum_{i=1}^{m} q_i a_{ij} \geq 0 \quad \text{for } j = 1, \ldots, n-1$$

and

2.4.10 $$\sum_{i=1}^{m} q_i(-a_{in}) < 0.$$

By 2.4.8, $q_i \geq 0$, and by 2.4.10, the q_i are not all zero. Hence we can let

$$x_i = \frac{q_i}{\sum_{j=1}^{m} q_j} \qquad i = 1, \ldots, m$$

and it follows directly from 2.4.9 and 2.4.10 that x is an optimal strategy for I such that $\sum x_i a_{in} > 0$.

Suppose, now, that $v(A) = k \neq 0$. As before, we construct a matrix $B = (b_{ij})$ where $b_{ij} = a_{ij} - k$; the proof proceeds exactly as in Theorem II.4.1.

II.5 COMPUTATION OF OPTIMAL STRATEGIES

Theorem II.4.1 (the minimax theorem) assures us that every two-person zero-sum game will have optimal strategies. Unfortunately, the proof given is an existence proof and does not explain how these optimal strategies are to be computed.

Here we give methods for solving the easiest games; Chapter III will deal with a more general method.

II.5.1 Saddle Points. The simplest case of all occurs if a saddle point exists, i.e., if there exists an entry a_{ij} which is both the maximum entry in its column and the minimum entry in its row. In this case, the pure strategies i and j, or equivalently, the mixed strategies x and y with $x_i = 1, y_j = 1$ and all other components equal to zero, will be optimal strategies for players I and II, respectively.

II.5.2 Domination. In a matrix A, we say the ith row *dominates* the kth row if

2.5.1 $\quad a_{ij} \geq a_{kj} \quad$ for all j

and

2.5.2 $\quad a_{ij} > a_{kj} \quad$ for at least one j.

Similarly, we say the jth column dominates the lth column if

2.5.3 $\quad a_{ij} \leq a_{il} \quad$ for all i

and

2.5.4 $\quad a_{ij} < a_{il} \quad$ for at least one i.

Briefly, a pure strategy (represented by its row or column) is said to dominate a second pure strategy if the choice of the first (dominating) strategy is at least as good as the choice of the second (dominated) strategy, and in some cases is better. It follows that a player can always dispense with any dominated strategies and use only the undominated strategies. The following theorem, which is given without proof, expresses this:

II.5.3 Theorem. Let A be a matrix game, and assume that the $i_1^{\text{th}}, i_2^{\text{th}}, \ldots, i_k^{\text{th}}$ rows of A are dominated. Then player I has an optimal strategy x such that $x_{i_1} = x_{i_2} = \cdots = x_{i_k} = 0$; moreover, any optimal strategy for the game obtained by removing the dominated rows will also be an optimal strategy for the original game.

A similar theorem will hold for row domination; the general effect of these theorems is that any dominated rows and columns may be discarded, allowing us to work with a smaller matrix.

II.5.4 Example. Consider the game with matrix

$$\begin{pmatrix} 2 & 0 & 1 & 4 \\ 1 & 2 & 5 & 3 \\ 4 & 1 & 3 & 2 \end{pmatrix}.$$

It is seen that the second column dominates the fourth column. It follows that player II will never use his fourth strategy; we can therefore disregard it and are left with the matrix

$$\begin{pmatrix} 2 & 0 & 1 & \not{4} \\ 1 & 2 & 5 & \not{3} \\ 4 & 1 & 3 & \not{2} \end{pmatrix}.$$

In this matrix, we find the third row dominates the first row. Removing this, we have

$$\begin{pmatrix} \not{2} & \not{0} & \not{1} & \not{4} \\ 1 & 2 & 5 & \not{3} \\ 4 & 1 & 3 & \not{2} \end{pmatrix}$$

and, in this matrix, we see that the third column is dominated by the second. Hence our matrix reduces to

$$\begin{pmatrix} 2 & 0 & 1 & 4 \\ 1 & 2 & 5 & 3 \\ 4 & 1 & 3 & 2 \end{pmatrix}$$

and we need only look for optimal strategies to the small 2×2 matrix game. The next section discusses such games.

II.5.5 2 × 2 Games. Suppose we are given the 2×2 matrix game

$$\begin{pmatrix} a_{11} & a_{12} \\ a_{21} & a_{22} \end{pmatrix}.$$

It may be that this game has a saddle point; if so, there is no problem. Suppose, however, that the game has no saddle point. It follows that the optimal strategies, $x = (x_1, x_2)$ and $y = (y_1, y_2)$ must have positive components. Now, if the value of the game is v, we have

$$a_{11}x_1y_1 + a_{12}x_1y_2 + a_{21}x_2y_1 + a_{22}x_2y_2 = v$$

or

2.5.5 $\quad x_1(a_{11}y_1 + a_{12}y_2) + x_2(a_{21}y_1 + a_{22}y_2) = v.$

Now, the two terms in parentheses on the left side of 2.5.5 are both less than or equal to v, since y is by hypothesis an optimal strategy. Suppose one of them were less than v; i.e., suppose

2.5.6 $\quad a_{11}y_1 + a_{12}y_2 < v$

2.5.7 $\quad a_{21}y_1 + a_{22}y_2 \leq v.$

Then, since $x_1 > 0$ and $x_1 + x_2 = 1$, the left hand term in 2.5.5 would be strictly smaller than v. It follows that both the terms in parentheses in 2.5.5 must equal v. Hence,

2.5.8 $\quad a_{11}y_1 + a_{12}y_2 = v$

2.5.9 $\quad a_{21}y_1 + a_{22}y_2 = v.$

Similarly, it can be seen that

2.5.10 $\quad a_{11}x_1 + a_{21}x_2 = v$

2.5.11 $\quad a_{12}x_1 + a_{22}x_2 = v$

or, in matrix form,

$$2.5.12 \quad Ay^t = \begin{pmatrix} v \\ v \end{pmatrix}$$

$$2.5.13 \quad xA = (v, v).$$

These equations, together with the equations

$$2.5.14 \quad x_1 + x_2 = 1$$

$$2.5.15 \quad y_1 + y_2 = 1$$

allow us to solve for x, y, and v. In fact, if A is non-singular, we will have

$$x = vJA^{-1}$$

where J is the vector (1, 1). We now eliminate v by noticing that the sum of the components of x, i.e., xJ^t, must be equal to 1; this gives

$$vJA^{-1}J^t = 1$$

or

$$2.5.16 \quad v = \frac{1}{JA^{-1}J^t}$$

and

$$2.5.17 \quad x = \frac{JA^{-1}}{JA^{-1}J^t}.$$

Similarly, we find

$$2.5.18 \quad y = \frac{A^{-1}J^t}{JA^{-1}J^t}.$$

In case A is singular, this is of course meaningless; it is easy then to see that

$$2.5.19 \quad x = \frac{JA^*}{JA^*J^t}$$

and

$$2.5.20 \quad y = \frac{A^*J^t}{JA^*J^t}$$

(where A^* is the adjoint of A) will give optimal strategies; note that 2.5.19 and 2.5.20 coincide with 2.5.17 and 2.5.18 when A is non-singular. We also see that

$$2.5.21 \quad v = \frac{|A|}{JA^*J^t}$$

where $|A|$ is the 'eterminant of A, will give the value of the game, whether A is singular or not. We recapitulate these laws in the following theorem:

II.5.6 Theorem. Let A be a 2×2 matrix game. Then if A does not have a saddle point, its unique optimal strategies and value will be given by

2.5.22 $$x = \frac{JA^*}{JA^*J^t}$$

2.5.23 $$y = \frac{A^*J^t}{JA^*J^t}$$

2.5.24 $$v = \frac{|A|}{JA^*J^t}$$

where A^* is the adjoint of A, $|A|$ the determinant of A, and J the vector $(1, 1)$.

II.5.7 Example. Solve the matrix game

$$\begin{pmatrix} 1 & 0 \\ -1 & 2 \end{pmatrix}.$$

It is easily checked that the game has no saddle point. Now, the adjoint of A is $A^* = \begin{pmatrix} 2 & 0 \\ 1 & 1 \end{pmatrix}$, and $|A| = 2$, $JA^* = (3, 1)$; $A^*J^t = (2, 2)$ and $JA^*J^t = 4$. Thus we have

$$x = (\tfrac{3}{4}, \tfrac{1}{4})$$
$$y = (\tfrac{1}{2}, \tfrac{1}{2})$$
$$v = \tfrac{1}{2}.$$

It may be checked that these strategies x and y do indeed guarantee the payoff value of $\frac{1}{2}$.

II.5.8 2 × n and m × 2 Games. The simplest games to solve, after the 2×2 games, are those games in which one of the players has only two strategies ($2 \times n$ or $m \times 2$ games). We shall consider $2 \times n$ games here; a similar analysis may be used for $m \times 2$ games.

The first player's problem is to maximize

$$v(x) = \min_j \{a_{1j}x_1 + a_{2j}x_2\}.$$

Now, $x_1 = 1 - x_2$ and so we have

$$v(x) = \min_j \{(a_{2j} - a_{1j})x_2 + a_{1j}\}.$$

Thus $v(x)$ is the minimum of n linear functions of the single variable x_1; these can all be plotted and their minimum $v(x)$ is then maximized by graphic methods.

II.5.9 Example. Consider the game with matrix

$$\begin{pmatrix} 2 & 3 & 1 & 5 \\ 4 & 1 & 6 & 0 \end{pmatrix}.$$

The several functions $(a_{2j} - a_{1j})x_2 + a_{1j}$ are easily plotted if we notice that they must pass through the points $(0, a_{1j})$ and $(1, a_{2j})$.

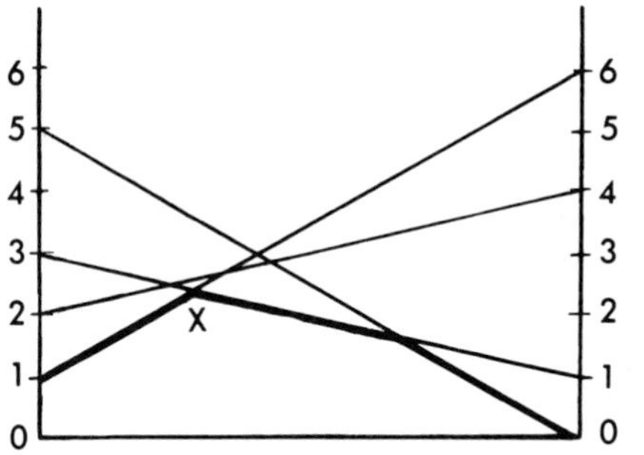

FIGURE II.5.1

The heavy irregular line represents the function $v(x)$. The highest point on this line, X, is seen to be at the intersection of the lines corresponding to the second and third columns. The abscissa at this point is $\frac{2}{7}$, the ordinate $\frac{17}{7}$. Thus we have $x = (\frac{5}{7}, \frac{2}{7})$ and $v = \frac{17}{7}$. These numbers could also be calculated by application of the formulas 2.5.22 and 2.5.24 to the 2×2 matrix consisting of the second and third columns of our game matrix. Application of 2.5.23 to this matrix also yields $y = (0, \frac{5}{7}, \frac{2}{7}, 0)$; it is easily checked that these are indeed the optimal strategies and value of the game.

This covers the simplest type of games; generalizations of

these methods for other games, while possible, are generally too laborious to be of practical use. For more general games, several schemes are in use. The easiest one to explain is given below. We do not give a proof of the scheme's validity; proofs of it may be found in the literature.

II.5.10 Solution by Fictitious Play. Let us suppose two players, perhaps with no knowledge of game theory, decide to play a game many times. While they might know nothing about game theory, they are nevertheless statistically inclined, and so keep track of the pure strategies used by their opponent at the several plays of the game. At each play, each player acts in such a way as to maximize his expected return against his opponent's observed empirical probability distribution: if player II has used his j^{th} strategy q_j times, player I will choose i so as to maximize $\sum_j a_{ij}q_j$. Similarly, if player I has played his i^{th} strategy p_i times, player II will choose j so as to minimize $\sum_i a_{ij}p_i$.

Now, naïve as this method of play may seem, the amazing fact is that the empirical distributions will converge to optimal strategies. More precisely, let p_i^N be the number of times that player I uses his i^{th} strategy during the first N plays of the game. If we let $x_i^N = p_i^N/N$, it is obvious that x^N is a mixed strategy. This sequence of strategies, x^N, need not converge; however, lying in the compact set of mixed strategies, it must have a convergent subsequence. The fact is that *the limit of any convergent subsequence will be an optimal strategy.*

We omit the proof of this theorem, as it is much too involved for our present purposes. Briefly, it is based on the fact that, if x^N and y^N are the strategies obtained as explained above for players I and II, respectively, the equation

2.5.25 $$\lim_{N\to\infty} \{v(y^N) - v(x^N)\} = 0$$

will hold. This method, incidentally, is most useful in the case of very large games (i.e., games with large numbers of pure strategies) which are, because of their size, difficult to handle in any other way. (See Problem II.9 for an outline of the proof of this theorem.)

II.6 SYMMETRIC GAMES

Let us conclude this chapter with a brief discussion of a special type of game.

II.6.1 Definition. A square matrix $A = (a_{ij})$ is said to be *skew-symmetric* if $a_{ij} = -a_{ji}$ for all i, j. A matrix game is said to be *symmetric* if its matrix is skew-symmetric.

II.6.2 Theorem. The value of a symmetric game is zero. Moreover, if x is an optimal strategy for I, then it is also optimal for II.

PROOF: Let A be the game matrix, and let x be any strategy. It is easy to see that $A = -A^t$. Hence,

$$\begin{aligned} xAx^t &= -xA^tx^t \\ &= -(xAx^t)^t \\ &= -xAx^t. \end{aligned}$$

Therefore, $xAx^t = 0$. It follows that, for any x,

$$\min_y xAy^t \leq 0$$

so that the value is non-positive, while

$$\max_y yAx^t \geq 0$$

so that the value is non-negative. Hence the value is zero. If, now, x is an optimal strategy for I, we have

$$xA \geq 0.$$

But this means

$$x(-A^t) \geq 0$$

and so

$$xA^t \leq 0$$

or

$$Ax^t \leq 0.$$

Hence x is also optimal for II.

An iterative algorithm, somewhat related to that given in II.5.10 above, has been devised for solving symmetric games.

Unlike the method of II.5.10, which gives a discrete sequence of strategies, this one relies on a continuous modification of the given strategy, which, in the limit, will approach optimality. The method, that of von Neumann and Brown, is, however, of very limited value (other than as a constructive existence proof of the minimax theorem) because the differential equations which it involves generally cannot be solved analytically.

II.6.3 Example. Consider the game with matrix

$$\begin{pmatrix} 0 & 1 & -2 \\ -1 & 0 & 3 \\ 2 & -3 & 0 \end{pmatrix}$$

It can be considered a generalization of the well-known children's game: "scissors, stone, and paper." As the matrix is skew-symmetric, we know the value of the game must be zero. Now, it is clear that the game has no saddle point. Nor can an optimal strategy use only two of the pure strategies, for if, say $x_1 > 0$, $x_2 > 0$ and $x_3 = 0$, it is easily seen that this mixed strategy of I gives a negative expectation against II's first pure strategy. Thus the optimal strategy x must have all positive components. This is also optimal for player II, and an argument similar to that given in II.5.5 above shows that x must satisfy the system of linear equations:

$$\begin{aligned} -x_2 + 2x &= 0 \\ x_1 \qquad + 3x_3 &= 0 \\ -2x_1 + 3x_2 \qquad &= 0 \\ x_1 + x_2 + x_3 &= 1. \end{aligned}$$

The solution to these equations is easily found: it is $(\frac{1}{2}, \frac{1}{3}, \frac{1}{6})$. This is the unique optimal strategy for both players.

PROBLEMS

1. Show that, if C is any convex set, and x is any point on the boundary of C, then there exists a vector $p \neq 0$ such that $\sum x_i p_i = 0$, and, for all $y \in C$, $\sum y_i p_i \geq 0$. (This is a somewhat stronger version of the theorem of the supporting hyperplane. Use this theorem, together with the fact that as x is on the

boundary of C, there exists a sequence of points $x^n \notin \overline{C}$ which converges to x.)

2. Show that the set of optimal strategies is always closed, convex, and bounded, and hence the convex hull of its extreme points.

3. Show that, if we treat an $m \times n$ matrix game as a point in mn-dimensional Euclidean space, the value of the game is a continuous function of the game.

4. Show that the set of optimal strategies of a game is a lower semi-continuous function of the game matrix.

5. Show that the set of $m \times n$ matrix games with unique optimal strategies is dense and open.

6. Let x and y be extreme points of the sets of optimal strategies of a matrix game, M, with non-zero value. Show that M has a square non-singular sub-matrix, $\dot{M}$, such that

$$\dot{x} = \frac{\dot{J}\dot{M}^{-1}}{\dot{J}\dot{M}^{-1}\dot{J}^t}$$

$$\dot{y}^t = \frac{\dot{M}^{-1}\dot{J}^t}{\dot{J}\dot{M}^{-1}\dot{J}^t}$$

$$v = \frac{1}{\dot{J}\dot{M}^{-1}\dot{J}^t}$$

where $\dot{J}$ is the vector, all of whose components are 1, of desired size:

(a) The product of x with any column of M that belongs to $\dot{M}$ must be v.

(b) The product of y with any row of M that belongs to $\dot{M}$ must be v.

(c) The ith row and the jth column of M must belong to $\dot{M}$ if $x_i > 0$ and $y_j > 0$.

(d) Rows and columns can be added to M, subject to (a) and (b) above, so long as they are linearly independent.

(e) If the matrix formed in this manner has linearly dependent rows, then x is not extreme. If the columns are linearly dependent, then y is not extreme.

7. Let $A = (a_{ij})$ be a skew-symmetric game matrix. Let $x = (x_1, \ldots, x_m)$ be a mixed strategy, and use the notation

$$u_i = \sum_{j=1}^{m} a_{ij}x_j$$

$$\varphi(u_i) = \max(0, u_i)$$

$$\Phi(x) = \sum_{i=1}^{m} \varphi(u_i)$$

$$\psi(x) = \sum_{i=1}^{m} \varphi^2(u_i).$$

Show that, for any "initial" strategy, x^0, the solution to the system of differential equations

$$\frac{dx_i}{dt} = \varphi(u_i) - x_i\Phi(x)$$
$$x(0) = x^0$$

converges to an optimal strategy, in the sense that it must have accumulation points, and any accumulation point is optimal:

(a) if x^0 is a strategy, then $x(t)$ will be a strategy for all t.

(b) The function ψ satisfies

$$\frac{d\psi}{dt} = -2\Phi(x)\psi(x)$$

(c) $\psi(x) \leq \Phi^2(x)$

(d) From (b) and (c), we must have

$$\psi(x) \leq \frac{\psi(x_0)}{(1 + t\sqrt{\psi(x_0)})^2}$$

8. Let $A = (a_{ij})$ be any $m \times n$ matrix, and consider the $mn \times mn$ matrix $B = (b_{pq})$ defined by

$$b_{(i-1)n+j,(k-1)n+l} = a_{il} - a_{kj}$$

Show that B is skew-symmetric and hence represents a symmetric game. Moreover, show that if $\lambda = (\lambda_1, \ldots, \lambda_{mn})$ is an optimal strategy for B, then the vectors x and y, defined by

$$x_i = \sum_{j=1}^{n} \lambda_{(i-1)n+j}$$

and

$$y_j = \sum_{i=1}^{m} \lambda_{(i-1)n+j}$$

are optimal strategies for players I and II, respectively, in A.

9. (Solutions of games by fictitious play.) Consider the following procedure for a matrix game $A = (a_{ij})$. Two players play the game a large number of times. At the first play, they may use any of their strategies. Suppose, now, that in the first k plays, I has used his i^{th} strategy X_i^k times $(i = 1, \ldots, m)$ while II has used his j^{th} strategy Y_j^k times $(j = 1, \ldots, n)$. Then, at the $(k+1)^{\text{th}}$ play, I will use his ${i_{k+1}}^{\text{th}}$ strategy, and II his ${j_{k+1}}^{\text{th}}$ strategy, where

$$\sum_j a_{i_{k+1},j} Y_j^k = \max_i \sum_j a_{ij} Y_j^k = U_k$$

and

$$\sum_i a_{i,j_{k+1}} X_i^k = \min_j \sum_i a_{ij} X_i^k = V_k$$

(Thus, at each play, each plays whatever is best against his opponent's cumulative past choices.) Show that any accumulation point of the sequence X^k/k, Y^k/k is a solution of the game A.

(a) We say the i_0^{th} row is eligible in the interval $[k, k']$ if there is a k_1, $k \leq k_1 \leq k'$ such that

$$\sum_j a_{i_0 j} Y_j^{k_1} = U_{k_1}$$

and similarly, the j_0^{th} column is eligible in $[k,k']$ if there is a k_2, $k \leq k_2 \leq k'$ such that

$$\sum_i a_{i j_0} X_i^{k_2} = V_{k_2}$$

Then, if all rows are eligible for $[k, l]$, we have

$$V_l - U_l \leq 4a(k - l)$$

where $a = \max |a_{ij}|$.

(b) For any $\varepsilon > 0$, there exists k_0 such that $V_k - U_k \leq k\varepsilon$ for all $k \geq k_0$. Prove by induction on the size of the matrix:

If A is a 1×1 matrix, this is obvious. Assume true for all submatrices $\tilde{A}$ of A. Choose k^* so that $V_{k^*} - U_{k^*} \leq k\varepsilon/2$ for all $\tilde{A}$. Then $k_0 \geq 8ak^*/\varepsilon$ will suffice. (Show that if some row or column is ineligible for an interval, it may effectively be discarded for that interval, treating only the remaining sub-matrix; consider intervals of the form $(k, k + k^*)$ with $k + k^* \leq k_0$.)

CHAPTER III

LINEAR PROGRAMMING

III.1 INTRODUCTION

A linear program is, briefly, the problem of maximizing (or minimizing) a linear function (called the *objective function*) subject to linear constraints. In the most common case, the constraints are loose inequalities, and the variables are restricted to non-negative values. Thus the most common form will be: find $(x_1, \ldots, x_m)$ so as to

3.1.1 Maximize $\sum_{i=1}^{m} c_i x_i$

subject to

3.1.2 $\sum a_{ij} x_i \leq b_j \qquad j = 1, \ldots, n$

3.1.3 $x_i \geq 0$

or, in matrix notation,

3.1.4 Maximize xC^t

subject to

3.1.5 $xA \leq B$

3.1.6 $x \geq 0.$

It should be pointed out that this is not the most general type of linear program. In fact, we may be asked to minimize the objective function, rather than to maximize it. Some of the constraints may be equations, and some of the variables may be allowed to take on negative values. However, it can also be pointed out that minimizing a function is the same as maximizing its negative, that an equation can be replaced by two opposite inequalities, and that an unrestricted variable can be expressed as the difference of two non-negative variables. Thus there is no loss in generality, strictly speaking, in considering programs such as (3.1.1)–(3.1.6).

III.1.1 Definition. The set of all points satisfying the constraints 3.1.2 and 3.1.3 shall be called the *constraint set* of program (3.1.1)–(3.1.3). The maximum of 3.1.1 is called the *value* of the program.

It may be seen that the solution of a matrix game can be reduced to a linear program. In fact, if player I uses the strategy $(x_1, \ldots, x_m)$ he can assure himself of an expectation at least equal to λ, where λ is any number such that

$$\sum a_{ij}x_i \geq \lambda \qquad \text{for } j = 1, \ldots, n.$$

Thus the problem of obtaining an optimal strategy for I reduces to the program:

3.1.7 Maximize λ

subject to

3.1.8 $-\sum_{j=1}^{n} a_{ij}x_i + \lambda \leq 0 \qquad j = 1, \ldots, n$

3.1.9 $\sum_{i=1}^{m} x_i = 1$

3.1.10 $x_i \geq 0 \qquad i = 1, \ldots, m.$

Similarly, the problem for II reduces to the program:

3.1.11 Minimize μ

subject to

3.1.12 $-\sum_{i=1}^{m} a_{ij}y_j + \mu \geq 0 \qquad i = 1, \ldots, m$

3.1.13 $\sum_{j=1}^{n} y_j = 1$

$y_j \geq 0 \qquad j = 1, \ldots, n.$

III.2 DUALITY

Consider the two linear programs:

3.2.1 Maximize xC^t

subject to

3.2.2 $xA \leq B$

3.2.3 $x \geq 0$

and

3.2.4 Minimize By^t

subject to

3.2.5 $yA^t \geq C$

3.2.6 $y \geq 0.$

The program (3.2.4)–(3.2.6) is said to be the *dual* of (3.2.1)–(3.2.3). Moreover, if we change the signs of A, B, and C, (3.2.4)–(3.2.6) can be rewritten as a maximization program:

3.2.7 Maximize $y(-B)^t$

subject to

3.2.8 $y(-A^t) \leq -C$

3.2.9 $y \geq 0.$

The dual of (3.2.7)–(3.2.9), as defined above, must be:

3.2.10 Minimize $-Cx^t$

subject to

3.2.11 $x(-A) \geq -B$

3.2.12 $x \geq 0.$

But it is clear that (3.2.10)–(3.2.12) is equivalent to (3.2.1)–(3.2.3). Hence we may state: the dual of (3.2.4)–(3.2.6) is (3.2.1)–(3.2.3). Duality is, then, a reciprocal relation: the two programs (3.2.1)–(3.2.3) and (3.2.4)–(3.2.6) are dual to each other.

The following theorems explain the relation between dual linear programs.

III.2.1 Theorem. Let x and y be in the constraint sets of programs (3.2.1)–(3.2.3) and (3.2.4)–(3.2.6) respectively. Then

3.2.13 $xC^t \leq By^t$.

PROOF: We have:

$$\begin{aligned} xC^t &= \sum_{i=1}^{m} x_i c_i \\ &\leq \sum_{i=1}^{m} x_i(\sum a_{ij} y_j) \qquad \text{(by 3.2.3 and 3.2.5)} \\ &= \sum_{j=1}^{m}\left(\sum_{i=1}^{n} x_i a_{ij}\right) y_j \\ &\leq \sum_{j=1}^{n} b_j y_j = By^t \qquad \text{(by 3.2.2 and 3.2.6).} \end{aligned}$$

III.2.2 Corollary. Suppose the vectors x^* and y^* are in the constraint sets of (3.2.1)–(3.2.3) and (3.2.4)–(3.2.6) respectively, and $x^*C^t = By^{*t}$. Then x^* and y^* are the solutions of the two programs.

In general, a linear program need not have a solution. One of two things may go wrong. It may be that the constraints are inconsistent so that the constraint set is empty, in which case the program is said to be *infeasible.* Or it may be that the desired maximum (or minimum) does not exist even if the program is *feasible,* since the function may take on arbitrarily large (or small, in the case of a minimization problem) values in the constraint set. For example, the program

$$\text{Maximize } 2x$$

subject to

$$\begin{aligned} -x &\leq 1 \\ x &\geq 0 \end{aligned}$$

does not have a solution, as the objective function can be made arbitrarily large. Such a program is said to be *unbounded.*

Let us consider the following corollary:

III.2.3 Corollary (to III.2.1). If the linear program (3.2.1)–(3.2.3) is unbounded, then the dual program (3.2.4)–(3.2.6) is infeasible. Similarly, if (3.2.4)–(3.2.6) is unbounded, then (3.2.1)–(3.2.3) is infeasible.

PROOF: Suppose (3.2.4)–(3.2.6) is feasible, i.e., suppose y is in the constraint set of (3.2.4)–(3.2.6). Then the objective function xC^t is bounded above by By^t. Hence (3.2.1)–(3.2.3) is not unbounded.

The converse of Corollary III.2.3 is not true. That is, if a program is infeasible, it does not follow that its dual is unbounded. It may be that both programs are infeasible.

III.2.4 Example. The dual programs

$$\text{Maximize } 5x_1 + x_2$$

subject to

$$x_1 - x_2 \leq 1$$

$$-x_1 + x_2 \leq -2$$

$$x_1, x_2 \geq 0$$

and

$$\text{Minimize } y_1 - 2y_2$$

subject to

$$y_1 - y_2 \geq 5$$

$$-y_1 + y_2 \geq 1$$

$$y_1, y_2 \geq 0$$

are both infeasible.

Thus, if a program is infeasible its dual may be unbounded, or it may also be infeasible. We shall prove next that these are the only possibilities.

III.2.5 Theorem. Let the program (3.2.1)–(3.2.3) be feasible, and suppose the dual program (3.2.4)–(3.2.6) is infeasible. Then (3.2.1)–(3.2.3) is unbounded.

PROOF: Suppose (3.2.4)–(3.2.6) is infeasible. We consider the game with the $m \times (n + 1)$ matrix

3.2.14 $(-A \mid C^t)$

which is obtained by adjoining the column vector C^t to the matrix $-A$. Suppose that the value of this game is negative. Then, if $s = (s_1, \ldots, s_n, s_{n+1})$ is an optimal strategy for II, we find that

$$-\sum_{j=1}^{n} a_{ij}s_j + c_i s_{n+1} < 0 \qquad i = 1, \ldots, m.$$

Now, if $s_{n+1} = 0$, we have

$$\sum_{j=1}^{n} a_{ij}s_j > 0 \qquad i = 1, \ldots, m$$

and so, for large enough k, we will have

$$\sum_{j=1}^{n} a_{ij}(ks_j) > c_i \qquad i = 1, \ldots, m$$
$$ks_j \geq 0$$

i.e., the vector ks satisfies 3.2.5 and 3.2.6, so that (3.2.4)–(3.2.6) is feasible. If, on the other hand, $s_{n+1} > 0$, we write $y_j = s_j/s_{n+1}$, and it follows that y satisfies 3.2.5 and 3.2.6. Thus *the value of the game must be zero or positive.*

Suppose now that the value of the game is zero; suppose also that II has an optimal strategy s with $s_{n+1} > 0$. Once again, if we set $y_j = s_j/s_{n+1}$, we find that y satisfies 3.2.5 and 3.2.6, contradicting the hypothesis that (3.2.4)–(3.2.6) was infeasible.

Hence the value of the matrix game 3.2.14 is non-negative. Moreover, if the value is zero, all optimal strategies s for player II must have $s_{n+1} = 0$.

By Theorems II.4.3 and II.5.3, it follows that player I must have a strategy $t = (t_1, \ldots, t_m)$ such that

$$\sum_{i=1}^{m} (-a_{ij})t_i \geq 0 \qquad j = 1, \ldots, n$$
$$\sum_{i=1}^{m} c_i t_i > 0.$$

By hypothesis, (3.2.1)–(3.2.3) is feasible. Suppose that $x = (x_1, \ldots, x_m)$ lies in its constraint set. Then, for every positive number α, the vector $x + \alpha t$ will also lie in the constraint set. Moreover,

$$(x + \alpha t)C^t = xC^t + \alpha t C^t$$

and the right side of this equation can be made as large as desired simply by increasing α. Thus (3.2.1)–(3.2.3) is unbounded.

We see thus that there are four possibilities for the dual pair of programs, (3.2.1)–(3.2.3) and (3.2.4)–(3.2.6). They can both be infeasible, or one can be infeasible while the other is unbounded, or both may be feasible and bounded. In this last case, the fact that the constraint set is closed assures us that the programs will both have solutions. The following very important theorem explains the relationship between them in this last case.

III.2.6 Theorem. Let the two dual programs (3.2.1)–(3.2.3) and (3.2.4)–(3.2.6) both be feasible. Then both will have solutions, x^* and y^* respectively, and, moreover,

$$x^*C^t = By^{*t};$$

i.e., both programs have the same value.

PROOF: Consider the game with matrix

$$M = \begin{pmatrix} 0 & A^t & -B^t \\ -A & 0 & C^t \\ B & -C & 0 \end{pmatrix}$$

where the 0's represent matrices of suitable size, all of whose entries are zero. The matrix M is skew-symmetric and therefore its value is zero.

Suppose now that $s = (s_1, \ldots, s_{m+n+1})$ is an optimal strategy for player I. We write:

$$\begin{aligned} y &= (s_1, \ldots, s_n) \\ x &= (s_{n+1}, \ldots, s_{n+m}) \\ w &= s_{n+m+1}. \end{aligned}$$

Because of the optimality of s, and since the game has value zero, we have:

$$\begin{aligned} -xA + wB &\geq 0 \\ yA^t \qquad - wC &\geq 0 \\ -yB^t + xC^t \qquad &\geq 0. \end{aligned}$$

Let us suppose that $w > 0$. If we set $x^* = x/w$ and $y^* = y/w$, it is clear that

$$\begin{aligned} x^*A &\leq B \\ y^*A^t &\geq C \\ x^*, y^* &\geq 0 \end{aligned}$$

and

$$x^*C^t \geq y^*B^t.$$

Now this means that x^* and y^* lie in the constraint sets of (3.2.1)–(3.2.3) and (3.2.4)–(3.2.6). By Theorem III.2.1 and its

Corollary III.2.2 it follows that x^* and y^* are the solutions to the two programs and, moreover,

$$x^*C^t = y^*B^t.$$

Suppose, on the other hand, that none of the optimal strategies s for player I has $s_{m+n+1} > 0$. In this case, by Theorem II.5.3, player II will have an optimal strategy, $r = (r_1, \ldots, r_{m+n+1})$, whose inner product with the last row of M is negative. Because the two players have identical sets of optimal strategies, we must have $r_{n+m+1} = 0$. If we now set

$$y = (r_1, \ldots, r_n)$$
$$x = (r_{n+1}, \ldots, r_{m+n})$$

we shall have

$$-xA \geq 0$$
$$yA^t \geq 0$$
$$-yB^t + xC^t > 0$$

or, equivalently,

$$xA \leq 0$$
$$yA^t \geq 0$$

3.2.15 $\quad xC^t > yB^t.$

Now either the left side of 3.2.15 is positive or its right side is negative. Suppose that the left side is positive. By hypothesis (3.2.1)–(3.2.3) is feasible; suppose x' lies in its constraint set. It is easily seen that for any positive α, $x' + \alpha x$ also lies in the constraint set, while $(x' + \alpha x)C^t$ can be made as large as desired simply by increasing α. Thus (3.2.1)–(3.2.3) will be unbounded. But this means (3.2.4)–(3.2.6) is infeasible. Similarly, if the right side of 3.2.15 is negative, (3.2.4)–(3.2.6) is unbounded and (3.2.1)–(3.2.3) is infeasible. This contradiction proves the theorem.

III.3 SOLUTION OF LINEAR PROBLEMS

At first glance it might seem that a linear program may be solved by the methods of the calculus, setting the partial derivatives equal to zero. In fact, however, the objective function is linear, so that all its partial derivatives are constant; the solution to a linear program will generally be found on the boundary of the constraint set. The method which is generally used for solving linear programs is based on the following observations:

3.3.1 The constraint set is the intersection of several half-spaces; since each half-space is convex, the constraint set is a convex hyperpolyhedron.

3.3.2 Because the constraint set is convex and the objective function is linear, any local extremum of the function will be the global extremum.

3.3.3 Because the objective function is linear, the extremum will be obtained at one of the extreme points (vertices) of the constraint set (hyperpolyhedron).

Geometrically, the simplex method may be described as follows: One of the vertices of the hyperpolyhedron is found (this may be done analytically by solving a system of n equations given by the constraints). All the edges which meet at this vertex are considered. If the objective function cannot be improved by moving along any one of these edges, it follows that the given vertex is a local extremum, and hence (by remark 3.3.2) the global extremum. If, on the other hand, the objective function is improved along one of the edges, we follow this edge to the vertex which lies at its other end and repeat the procedure. Since the objective function is improved at each step, it follows that we cannot go through the same vertex twice. Since there are only a finite number of vertices, this procedure will bring us to the solution in a finite number of steps.

III.3.1 Example. We illustrate this notion with the example:

$$\text{Maximize } w = 2x + y$$

subject to

$$x \leq 1$$

$$y \leq 1$$

$$2x + 2y \leq 3$$

$$x, y \geq 0.$$

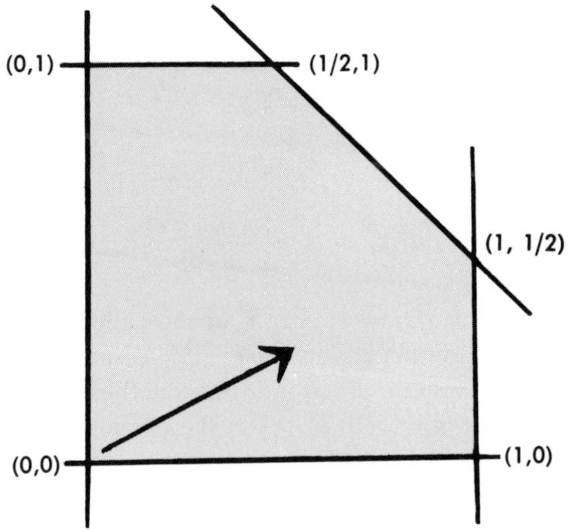

FIGURE III.3.1

The constraint set is shaded in the figure. The arrow shows the gradient of the objective function. If we start from the origin, we see that w is increased along either of the edges that start there. We take, say, the edge that goes to $(1, 0)$. At $(1, 0)$, we find that w is increased along the edge to $(1, \frac{1}{2})$. At this point, we find that w decreases along both edges that meet here. Thus we can conclude that $(1, \frac{1}{2})$ is the solution of our program.

III.4 THE SIMPLEX ALGORITHM

Let us describe algebraically the method given above.

We introduce a schematic notation, the purpose of which is simply to achieve a small degree of economy in symbols. Let us suppose we are given the system of inequalities

$$
\begin{aligned}
&a_{11}x_1 + a_{21}x_2 + \cdots + a_{m1}x_m \leq b_1 \\
&a_{12}x_1 + a_{22}x_2 + \cdots + a_{m2}x_m \leq b_2 \qquad (3.4.1) \\
&\cdot \quad \cdot \quad \cdot \quad \cdot \quad \cdot \quad \cdot \quad \cdot \quad \cdot \quad \cdot \quad \cdot \\
&a_{1n}x_1 + a_{2n}x_2 + \cdots + a_{mn}x_m \leq b_n
\end{aligned}
$$

which, together with the usual non-negativity constraints, characterizes the constraint set of some linear program. We can rewrite these in the form

$$
\begin{array}{ll}
& a_{11}x_1 + a_{21}x_2 + \cdots + a_{m1}x_m - b_1 = -u_1 \\
3.4.2 & a_{12}x_1 + a_{22}x_2 + \cdots + a_{m2}x_m - b_2 = -u_2 \\
& \cdots\cdots\cdots\cdots\cdots\cdots \\
& a_{1n}x_1 + a_{2n}x_2 + \cdots + a_{mn}x_m - b_n = -u_n
\end{array}
$$

where the u_j, $j = 1, \ldots, n$, are so-called *slack* variables, restricted to take non-negative values. The constraints of 3.4.1 reduce now to this system of equations, together with the non-negativity constraints $x_i \geq 0$, $u_j \geq 0$. We propose to identify the system of equations 3.4.2 with the schema:

$$
3.4.3 \quad
\begin{array}{ccccc|l}
x_1 & x_2 & \cdots & x_m & 1 & \\
\hline
a_{11} & a_{21} & \cdots & a_{m1} & -b_1 & = -u_1 \\
a_{12} & a_{22} & \cdots & a_{m2} & -b_2 & = -u_2 \\
\cdot & \cdot & \cdots & \cdot & \cdot & \cdots \\
a_{1n} & a_{2n} & \cdots & a_{mn} & -b_n & = -u_n. \\
\hline
\end{array}
$$

Thus each row inside the box of such a schema represents the linear equation obtained by multiplying each entry in the row by the term in the top row (outside the box) and corresponding column, and setting their sum equal to the term outside the box, on the right. The principal advantage of such a scheme, as explained previously, is that it avoids repetition of the variables $x_1, \ldots, x_m$, and thus saves much space. It is also possible to introduce the objective function into the schema 3.4.3 by calling it, say, w, and adjoining the row

$$
3.4.4 \quad
\begin{array}{|ccccc|l}
c_1 & c_2 & \cdots & c_m & 0 & = w \\
\hline
\end{array}
$$

at the bottom of the schema.

If we do this, it may be seen that the schema which gives the linear program (3.2.1)–(3.2.3) can also be used to give the dual program (3.2.4)–(3.2.6). In fact, we can use the columns to represent the equations of system 3.2.5, obtaining the double schema

3.4.5
$$\begin{array}{c|cccc|c|l}
 & x_1 & x_2 & \cdots & x_m & 1 & \\
\hline
y_1 & a_{11} & a_{21} & \cdots & a_{m1} & -b_1 & = -u_1 \\
y_2 & a_{12} & a_{22} & \cdots & a_{m2} & -b_2 & = -u_2 \\
\cdot\ \cdot & \cdot & \cdot & \cdots & \cdot & \cdot\ \cdot & \cdot\ \cdot\ \cdot\ \cdot \\
y_n & a_{1n} & a_{2n} & \cdots & a_{mn} & -b_n & = -u_n \\
\hline
-1 & c_1 & c_2 & \cdots & c_m & 0 & = w \\
\hline
 & \parallel & \parallel & & \parallel & \parallel & \\
 & v_1 & v_2 & \cdots & v_m & -w' &
\end{array}$$

which gives the two dual programs, (3.2.1)–(3.2.3) and (3.2.4)–(3.2.6), simultaneously.

Consider next the maximizing problem (3.2.1)–(3.2.3) as represented by the rows of schema 3.4.5. We have a system of $n + 1$ equations in the $m + n + 1$ unknowns $x_1, \ldots, x_m, u_1, \ldots, u_n$, and w. We can, in general, solve for $n + 1$ of these unknowns in terms of the remaining m. The schema, of course, represents a solution for $u_1, \ldots, u_n$, and w in terms of the x_i's, but, except in degenerate cases, which involve the inversion of a singular matrix, we can solve for any $n + 1$ in terms of the other m.

Suppose that we have solved for the $n + 1$ variables $s_1, s_2, \ldots, s_n, w$, in terms of the variables $r_1, r_2, \ldots, r_m$, and obtain the new schema (simplex tableau)

3.4.6
$$\begin{array}{cccc|c|l}
r_1 & r_2 & \cdots & r_m & 1 & \\
\hline
a'_{11} & a'_{21} & \cdots & a'_{m1} & -b'_1 & = -s_1 \\
a'_{12} & a'_{22} & \cdots & a'_{m2} & -b'_2 & = -s_2 \\
\cdot & \cdot & \cdots & \cdot & \cdot\ \cdot & \cdot\ \cdot\ \cdot\ \cdot \\
a'_{1n} & a'_{2n} & \cdots & a'_{mn} & -b'_n & = -s_n \\
\hline
c'_1 & c'_2 & \cdots & c'_m & \delta & = w \\
\hline
\end{array}$$

where every entry in the bottom row (except possibly the right-hand entry δ) and every entry in the right-hand column (again excepting the bottom entry) is non-positive. If this happens, then the tableau 3.4.6 gives us the solution to program (3.2.1)–(3.2.3). In fact, if we let all the variables $r_1, \ldots, r_m$ be equal to zero, each of the variables s_j will be equal to the corresponding b. But the entries $-b_j$ are non-positive. Hence all the s_j will be non-negative. Since the r_i are all equal to zero, this point lies in the constraint set of (3.2.1)–(3.2.3). Moreover, the bottom row gives us the equation

$$w = c_1'r_1 + \cdots + c_m'r_m + \delta$$

where all the c_i' are non-negative. It is clear that the largest possible value of w will be obtained by setting all the r_i equal to zero (since they cannot be made smaller). Thus the solution of (3.2.1)–(3.2.3) is obtained from 3.4.6 by setting

3.4.7 $r_i = 0 \qquad i = 1, \ldots, m$

3.4.8 $s_j = b_j' \qquad j = 1, \ldots, n$

3.4.9 $w = \delta.$

We are looking for a method which will allow us to rewrite our system 3.4.5 in the form of 3.4.6, with non-positive entries along the right-hand column and bottom row (except possibly the bottom right-hand entry δ). We give first some definitions:

III.4.1 Definition. In the simplex tableau (schema) 3.4.6 the variables s_j are called the *basic* variables, while the variables r_i are called the non-basic variables.

III.4.2 Definition. A simplex tableau will also be called a *basic point.* If all the entries in the right-hand column (except possibly the bottom entry) are non-positive, it will be called a *basic feasible point* (b.f.p.). If all the entries in the bottom row (except possibly the right-hand entry) are non-positive, it will be called a *basic dual feasible point* (b.d.f.p.).

As already noted, when the right-hand entries are non-negative, we obtain a point in the constraint set of (3.2.1)–(3.2.3) by letting the non-basic variables vanish. This is what is meant by a b.f.p. If all the bottom entries are non-positive, we see that we get a point in the constraint set of the dual program (3.2.4)–(3.2.6). This is a b.d.f.p. Finally, if a b.f.p. is also a b.d.f.p., it is the solution to the program (as was noted above).

Geometrically, a basic feasible point represents a vertex of the convex hyperpolyhedron which is the constraint set of (3.2.1)–(3.2.3). As explained before, we are interested in looking at the edges which pass through this vertex, or, equivalently, at the vertices which lie at the other ends of these edges. A vertex is obtained by setting m of the variables (the non-basic ones) equal to zero; an edge is obtained by setting $m - 1$ of the variables equal to zero. An edge passes through a vertex if these $m - 1$ variables are among the m which correspond to the vertex. Thus two vertices lie on an edge if they have $m - 1$ of their non-basic variables in common, which brings us to the following definition:

III.4.3 Definition. Two basic points are said to be *adjacent* if they represent different points in space and their sets of basic variables differ by at most one.

It should be noticed that it is not impossible for two simplex tableaux to represent the same point even though their basic variables might be different. In fact, there is nothing to prevent the entries in the right-hand column from vanishing. If some such b'_j does vanish, the corresponding s_j will vanish when the non-basic variables vanish. Thus we could place it among the non-basic variables without changing the point represented by the tableau.

III.4.4 Pivot Steps. A pivot step is a procedure for changing the sets of basic variables by one; i.e., it is a procedure for solving the $m + 1$ equations of 3.4.6 for $n - 1$ of the s_j's, one of the r_i's, and w in terms of the remaining m variables. Let us see how this is done.

Suppose we wish to make s_j a non-basic variable, while making r_i a basic variable. We take the equation

$$a_{1j}r_1 + a_{2j}r_2 + \cdots + a_{mj}r_m - b_j = -s_j$$

and solve for $-r_i$, obtaining

$$\frac{a_{1j}}{a_{ij}} r_1 + \cdots + \frac{a_{i-1,j}}{a_{ij}} r_{i-1} + \frac{1}{a_{ij}} s_j + \cdots + \frac{a_{mj}}{a_{ij}} r_m - \frac{b_j}{a_{ij}} = -r_i$$

(assuming, of course, that $a_{ij} \neq 0$). This new equation will be the jth row of our modified simplex tableau. To get the remaining rows, it is necessary to substitute this value of r_i. Thus (assuming that $j \neq 1$) the first equation will now be

$$\left(a_{11} - \frac{a_{1j}}{a_{ij}}\right)r_1 + \cdots + \left(a_{i-1,1} - \frac{a_{i-1,j}}{a_{ij}}\right)r_{i-1} - \frac{a_{1i}}{a_{ij}}s_j + \cdots - \left(b_1 - \frac{b_j}{a_{ij}}\right) = -s_1$$

and the other equations (except, of course, the jth equation) will be similarly changed. To get the new tableau, we simply modify the coefficients accordingly, and interchange the position of the two variables, r_i and s_j.

The entry a_{ij}, which cannot be zero, is called the *pivot* of the transformation. The transformation itself is called a *pivot step*. We can summarize the transformation most easily according to the diagram

3.4.10 $$\begin{bmatrix} p & q \\ r & s \end{bmatrix} \rightarrow \begin{bmatrix} \dfrac{1}{p} & \dfrac{q}{p} \\ -\dfrac{r}{p} & s - \dfrac{qr}{p} \end{bmatrix}.$$

In 3.4.10, p represents the pivot, q is any other entry in the pivot row, r is any other entry in the pivot column, and s is the entry in the row of r and the column of q. Thus, the pivot is replaced by its reciprocal, $1/p$. The remaining entries in the pivot row are simply divided by p, while the remaining entries in the pivot column are divided by p and change in sign. Finally, the other entries in the tableau are decreased by the product of the entries in the same row and pivot column, and in the same column and pivot row, divided by p.

III.4.5 Example. Given the simplex tableau:

3.4.11

	r_1	r_2	r_3	1	
	4	1	3	2	$= -s_1$
	−1*	2	−1	4	$= -s_2$
	1	2	2	0	$= -s_3$
	0	1	4	1	$= -s_4$

which represents a system of equations solved for s_1, s_2, s_3, s_4 in terms of r_1, r_2, r_3, we wish to solve the system for s_1, r_1, s_3, s_4 in terms of s_2, r_2, r_3. The pivot, then, will be the starred entry which lies below r_1 and to the left of s_2. Performing the transformation given by 3.4.10, and interchanging the position of r_1 and s_2, we obtain the tableau

3.4.12

s_2	r_2	r_3	1	
4	9	−1	18	$= -s_1$
−1	−2	1	−4	$= -r_1$
1	4	1	4	$= -s_3$
0	1	4	1	$= -s_4.$

It may be checked that the system of equations 3.4.12 is equivalent to the system 3.4.11.

The Dual Problem. In III.4.4, above, we determined the form of the transformation which must be effected on the simplex tableau in order that the system of equations represented by the rows of the new tableau be equivalent to that represented by the old tableau. On the other hand, we had mentioned above that the tableau can be used to represent a pair of dual programs simultaneously. It remains to be verified, then, that the equations represented by the columns of the tableau will also be equivalent to the old system.

The ith column of Tableau 3.4.5 represents the linear equation

$$\sum a_{ij} y_j - c_i = v_i.$$

Here, of course, it is the v_i's which are basic variables, while the y_j's are non-basic. Now, let us suppose we wish to interchange the role of v_i and y_j; i.e., we wish to make y_j a basic variable, while v_i is made non-basic. As before, we solve this equation for y_j in terms of v_i and the remaining y_j's, thus obtaining

$$-\frac{a_{i1}}{a_{ij}} y_1 + \cdots - \frac{a_{i,j-1}}{a_{ij}} y_{j-1} + \frac{1}{a_{ij}} v_i + \cdots + \frac{c_i}{a_{ij}} = y_j.$$

If we substitute this value of y_j in the remaining equations, we obtain for the first column (assuming of course $i \neq 1$)

$$\left(a_{11} - \frac{a_{i1}a_{1j}}{a_{ij}}\right)y_1 + \cdots + \frac{a_{1j}}{a_{ij}}v_i + \cdots - \left(c_1 - \frac{c_i a_{1j}}{a_{ij}}\right) = v_1$$

and so on for the other columns. If we represent these changes schematically, as in 3.4.10, we obtain the schema:

$$\begin{bmatrix} p & q \\ r & s \end{bmatrix} \rightarrow \begin{bmatrix} \dfrac{1}{p} & \dfrac{q}{p} \\ -\dfrac{r}{p} & s - \dfrac{qr}{p} \end{bmatrix}.$$

But this is precisely the schema 3.4.10. Thus the same transformation which preserves the (primal) problem (3.2.1)–(3.2.3) will preserve the dual problem (3.2.4)–(3.2.6). That is, each simplex tableau obtained by means of pivot steps will represent the pair of dual problems simultaneously.

III.5 THE SIMPLEX ALGORITHM (CONTINUED)

We have just explained the fundamental pivot step which is the basic tool of the simplex algorithm. What we need now, however, is a rule to decide how to use this tool. In fact, the simplex tableau will generally have a large number of non-zero entries which can be used as pivots; we need a rule to tell us which of these entries should be used as pivot.

When we refer to the geometric analogue, we note that each of our $m + n$ variables, $x_1, \ldots, x_m, u_1, \ldots, u_n$, can be thought of as representing a bounding hyperplane of our constraint set; i.e., the hyperplane in which that variable vanishes. Now the point of intersection of m of these hyperplanes (assuming these are independent) is a basic point of our constraint set. If all the other variables are also non-negative, the basic point is actually a b.f.p.; i.e., it will lie in the constraint set.

Our choice of pivot steps will have two objectives. First, starting from a basic point, we must move toward a b.f.p. Once we have a b.f.p., we must try to improve (increase or decrease) our objective function, being careful to keep at all times to b.f.p.'s, until a solution (i.e., a point where no further improvement is possible) has been reached. We thus give two sets of rules: The first, assuming nothing, will give us a b.f.p.; the second, assuming we start from a b.f.p., will give us a solution. Let us call these Case I and Case II, respectively.

III.5.1 Rules for Choosing a Pivot.

3.5.1 Case I. Let $-b_k$ be the lowest positive entry in the right-hand column (excepting possibly the bottom entry). Choose any negative entry, a_{i_0k}, in the kth row. The pivot will be in the $i_0{}^{\text{th}}$ column. Now, for all $j \geq k$, for which $-b_j/a_{i_0j}$ is negative, let j_0 be that value of j for which this quotient is largest (i.e., closest to zero). Then $a_{i_0j_0}$ will be our pivot. (If there is a tie, any one of those entries which give the maximum may be chosen.)

3.5.2 Case II. Let c_{i_0} be any positive entry in the bottom row (again, excepting possibly the right-hand entry). The pivot will be in the $i_0{}^{\text{th}}$ column. For all j, for which $-b_j/a_{i_0j}$ is negative, let j_0 be that value of j for which this quotient is greatest (i.e., closest to zero). Then $a_{i_0j_0}$ will be our pivot. (Again, in case of ties, we may choose as above.)

III.5.2 Proof of Convergence. We prove now that our algorithm will actually converge in a finite number of steps. We shall make the assumption of non-degeneracy, which means that no zeros will appear in either the bottom row or the right-hand column (again, excepting the right-hand bottom entry).

3.5.3 In Case I, we shall prove that all the entries in the right-hand column, below the kth, remain negative, while the kth entry itself decreases.

We know that, for each $j \neq j_0$, the entry $-b_j$ will be replaced by

$$-b'_j = -b_j + \frac{a_{i_0j}b_{j_0}}{a_{i_0j_0}}.$$

We also know that $-b_{j_0}/a_{i_0j_0}$ is negative. Hence, if $a_{i_0j} < 0$, it is clear that $-b'_j < -b_j$.

If, on the other hand, $a_{i_0j} > 0$, we know (by our rule) that, for $j \geq k$,

$$-\frac{b_{j_0}}{a_{i_0j_0}} \geq -\frac{b_j}{a_{i_0j}}.$$

Now,

$$-b'_j = a_{i_0j}\left(-\frac{b_j}{a_{i_0j}} + \frac{b_{j_0}}{a_{i_0j_0}}\right).$$

The term in parentheses will be non-positive. Hence $-b'_j < 0$.

Finally, we notice that $-b_{j_0}$ will be replaced by $-b_{j_0}/a_{i_0j_0}$, which is, by hypothesis, negative.

Thus for $j > k$, we see $b'_j < 0$. We also see $-b'_k < -b_k$. As there are only a finite number of possible simplex tableaux, we see that, if we continue to pivot according to our rule, we shall eventually reach a tableau in which, for $j \geq k$, $-b_j < 0$. We then work on the next higher row, etc., until all entries in the right-hand column are non-positive.

3.5.4 In Case II, we see that, by the same argument as above, each $-b_j$ will be replaced by $-b'_j$, where $-b'_j \leq 0$. The bottom right-hand entry, δ, will be replaced by:

$$\delta' = \delta + \frac{c_{i_0}b_{j_0}}{a_{i_0j_0}}.$$

We know that $c_{i_0} > 0$, while $-b_{j_0}/a_{i_0j_0} < 0$. Hence $\delta' > \delta$. Now, δ and δ' are the values of the objective function at the two given b.f.p.'s. Hence we see that the objective function is increased. As there are only a finite number of b.f.p.'s, it follows that we shall eventually reach the solution.

We have thus seen that (under the assumption of non-degeneracy), if we can continue to pivot according to the rules given in III.5.2, the simplex algorithm will give us the solution to the linear program in a finite number of steps. It may be, however, that the two rules, 3.5.3 and 3.5.4, will fail us. Two things could conceivably go wrong. In Case I, it may be that a row, ending in a positive entry, has only non-negative entries. In Case II, it may be that a column which has a positive entry in the bottom row has only non-positive entries otherwise. In either situation, it becomes impossible to follow the rules III.5.1. We shall see that such a situation implies the insolubility (either because of infeasibility or because of unboundedness) of the program.

Suppose, then, in Case I, that a row which ends in a positive entry has only non-negative entries. The row represents the equation

$$3.5.5 \quad \sum_{i=1}^{n} a_{ij}r_i - b_j = -s_j.$$

Now, the a_{ij} and r_i are all, by hypothesis, non-negative, while $-b_j$ is positive. But this means s_j must be negative. Thus the constraints are inconsistent; i.e., the program is infeasible.

In Case II, suppose we have a column with a positive entry in the bottom row, but all non-positive entries otherwise. Now, if the coefficient a_{ij} is non-positive, it follows from equation 3.5.5 that r_i can be increased indefinitely without decreasing s_j. As all the entries in the given column (except the bottom entry) are non-positive, it follows that we can increase r_i indefinitely, keeping all the other r's fixed at zero, without leaving the constraint set. But, as the bottom entry in this column is positive, this will increase the objective function indefinitely. Hence the program is unbounded.

Degeneracy. In the discussion above, an explicit assumption of non-degeneracy was made; i.e., we assumed that no zeros would ever appear in the right-hand column (except possibly for the bottom entry). Now, if zeros do appear, it is clear that certain strict inequalities, which were given above, must be replaced by loose inequalities. For example, the inequality $\delta' > \delta$, which characterizes the steps of Case II when non-degeneracy is assumed, must be replaced by the weaker $\delta' \geq \delta$. Now, $\delta' > \delta$ means that the objective function is increased at each step, and hence it is clear that we cannot pass through the same b.f.p. twice. This guarantees termination. The weaker $\delta' \geq \delta$ allows for the possibility that we might pivot several times, and, after all these pivots, reach the same tableau again.

Degeneracy of the program, as characterized by the appearance of zeros in the right-hand column, occurs when more than m of the variables vanish simultaneously, i.e., when more than m of the bounding hyperplanes of the constraint set pass through one point. Thus non-degeneracy will hold if the $m + n$ bounding hyperplanes are in general position in space. But this means that, in a degenerate program, an arbitrarily small perturbation of the constraints will remove the degeneracy.

A technique which is often used, then, is a perturbation technique. If one of the rows, then, ends in a zero: that is, if it looks like this:

$$|a_{1j} \quad a_{2j} \quad \cdots \quad a_{mj} \quad 0| = -s_j$$

we replace the variable s_j by the variable $s_j' = s_j + \varepsilon$, to obtain the row

$$|a_{1j} \quad a_{2j} \quad \cdots \quad a_{mj} \quad -\varepsilon| = -s_j'$$

where ε is assumed to be positive but very small. We proceed to solve the modified program by the simplex algorithm. Because these perturbations will remove any degeneracy, it follows that the program, as modified by this finite number of perturbations, will be solved (if it has a solution) in this manner. The solution will be a function of the various perturbations; i.e., the value of the $x_1, \ldots, x_m$ will depend on the particular values given to the ε's introduced in these perturbations. Generally, however, they depend linearly on these ε's; it is merely a question of setting these equal to zero, to obtain a solution to the original (unperturbed) problem.

In fact the perturbations, which replace the constraints $s_j \geq 0$ by the weaker constraints $s_j' \geq 0$, tend to enlarge the constraint set. We are interested in the extreme points of the constraint set; it is clear that the only ones affected by this perturbation are those for which $s_j = 0$. At each of these (and there are only a finite number) the perturbation will increase (or decrease) the objective function by some constant times ε. Suppose now that the solution to the program is at an extreme point P_1. There is some positive number η, such that, if P_2 is any other extreme point (not also a solution to the program), then $w(P_2) \leq w(P_1) - \eta$ (where $w(P)$ is the value of the objective function at the point P). It is clear that if all the ε's are small enough, the objective function cannot be increased by more than η at any extreme point. It follows that P_2 cannot be the solution to the perturbed problem because it was not the solution to the unperturbed problem. Thus the solution to the perturbed problem will always give us a solution to the unperturbed problem.

In general the perturbation method, while useful (especially in proving the finiteness of the simplex algorithm), is tedious, especially since one never knows how small the ε's must be to guarantee that the solution to the perturbed problem will solve the original problem. In computer work, it has been found easier to instruct the computer to work in a random manner whenever it has a choice of pivots. This guarantees, with probability 1, that the cycling which complicates the algorithm in such cases will be avoided (since in fact such cycling occurs only when there is a systematic method of choosing the pivot).

III.6 EXAMPLES

Let us now consider several examples of the solution of linear programs by the simplex method.

III.6.1 Example

Maximize $5x_1 + 2x_2 + x_3$

subject to

$$\begin{aligned} x_1 + 3x_2 - x_3 &\leq 6 \\ x_2 + x_3 &\leq 4 \\ 3x_1 + x_2 \quad &\leq 7 \\ x_1, x_2, x_3 &\geq 0 \end{aligned}$$

We form the tableau:

3.6.1

x_1	x_2	x_3	1	
1	3	-1	-6	$= -u_1$
0	1	1	-4	$= -u_2$
3*	1	0	-7	$= -u_3$
5	2	1	0	$= w.$

Because all the columns have positive entries in the bottom row, we can choose any column for our pivot. We may, for instance, choose the first column; the pivot will then be the starred entry. We pivot on it to obtain the tableau:

3.6.2

u_3	x_2	x_3	1	
$-\frac{1}{3}$	$\frac{8}{3}$	-1	$-\frac{11}{3}$	$= -u_1$
0	1	1*	-4	$= -u_2$
$\frac{1}{3}$	$\frac{1}{3}$	0	$-\frac{7}{3}$	$= -x_1$
$-\frac{5}{3}$	$\frac{1}{3}$	1	$\frac{35}{3}$	$= w.$

Again, we pivot on the starred entry; this gives us:

3.6.3

	u_3	x_2	u_2	1	
	$-\frac{1}{3}$	$\frac{11}{3}$	1	$-\frac{23}{3}$	$= -u_1$
	0	1	1	-4	$= -x_3$
	$\frac{1}{3}$	$\frac{1}{3}$	0	$-\frac{7}{3}$	$= -x_1$
	$-\frac{5}{3}$	$-\frac{2}{3}$	-1	$\frac{47}{3}$	$= w.$

Here it is clear that we have our solution: $(\frac{7}{3}, 0, 4)$. For this choice of variables, the value of w is $\frac{47}{3}$.

III.6.2 Example

Minimize $6y_1 + 4y_2 + 7y_3$

subject to

$$\begin{aligned} y_1 \qquad + 3y_3 &\geq 5 \\ 3y_1 + y_2 + y_3 &\geq 2 \\ -y_1 + y_2 \qquad &\geq 1 \\ y_1, y_2, y_3 &\geq 0. \end{aligned}$$

It is easily seen that this problem is the dual of III.6.1. If we had written Tableau 3.6.1 so as to incorporate both problems, and continued as above, the last tableau would be:

3.6.4

	u_3	x_2	u_2	1	
y_1	$-\frac{1}{3}$	$\frac{11}{3}$	1	$-\frac{23}{3}$	$= -u_1$
v_3	0	1	1	-4	$= -x_3$
v_1	$\frac{1}{3}$	$\frac{1}{3}$	0	$-\frac{7}{3}$	$= -x_1$
-1	$-\frac{5}{3}$	$-\frac{2}{3}$	-1	$\frac{47}{3}$	$= w.$
	$\Vert$	$\Vert$	$\Vert$	$\Vert$	
	y_3	v_2	y_2	w'	

Hence, the solution to III.6.2 is $(0, 1, \frac{5}{3})$. The value of this program is the same as III.6.1: i.e., $\frac{47}{3}$.

III.6.3 Example. Solve the matrix game:

$$\begin{pmatrix} 3 & 6 & 1 & 4 \\ 5 & 2 & 4 & 2 \\ 1 & 4 & 3 & 5 \end{pmatrix}.$$

SOLUTION: We write the maximizing problem in the form: Maximize λ

subject to

$$\begin{aligned} 3x_1 + 5x_2 + x_3 &\geq \lambda \\ 6x_1 + 2x_2 + 4x_3 &\geq \lambda \\ x_1 + 4x_2 + 3x_3 &\geq \lambda \\ 4x_1 + 2x_2 + 5x_3 &\geq \lambda \\ x_1 + x_2 + x_3 &= 1 \\ x_1, x_2, x_3 &\geq 0. \end{aligned}$$

This gives us the tableau:

3.6.5

x_1	x_2	x_3	λ	
−3	−5	−1	1	$= -u_1$
−6	−2	−4	1	$= -u_2$
−1	−4	−3	1	$= -u_3$
−4	−2	−5	1*	$= -u_4$
−1	−1	−1	0	$= -1.$

Here, we must pivot first in such a way as to put λ among the basic variables, and 1 among the non-basic. Unfortunately, the entry below λ and on the same row as 1 turns out to be a zero; we need, therefore, two pivot steps rather than one to do this.

In the following sequence, asterisks are used to denote the pivot at each step:

3.6.6

x_1	x_2	x_3	u_4	
1	−3	4	−1	$= -u_1$
−2	0	1	−1	$= -u_2$
3	−2	2	−1	$= -u_3$
−4	−2	−5	1	$= -\lambda$
−1	−1	−1*	0	$= -1$

3.6.7

x_1	x_2	1	u_4	
-3	-7	4	-1	$= -u_1$
-3	-1	1	-1	$= -u_2$
1	-4	2	-1	$= -u_3$
1	3	-5	1	$= -\lambda$
1	1	-1	0	$= -x_3.$

We now permute rows and columns so as to make the right-hand column correspond to the constant term, and the bottom row correspond to the objective function, λ. We also change all signs in the bottom row, obtaining the following tableau:

3.6.8

x_1	x_2	u_4	1	
-3	-7	-1	4	$= -u_1$
-3	-1	-1	1	$= -u_2$
1	-4	-1^*	2	$= -u_3$
1	1	0	-1	$= -x_3$
-1	-3	-1	5	$= \lambda.$

We proceed now according to the rules 3.5.1, until we reach a b.f.p.

3.6.9

x_1	x_2	u_3	1	
-4	-3	-1^*	2	$= -u_1$
-4	3	-1	-1	$= -u_2$
-1	4	-1	-2	$= -u_4$
1	1	0	-1	$= -x_3$
-2	1	-1	3	$= \lambda$

3.6.10

x_1	x_2	u_1	1	
4	3	-1	-2	$= -u_3$
0	6^*	-1	-3	$= -u_2$
3	7	-1	-4	$= -u_4$
1	1	0	-1	$= -x_3$
2	4	-1	1	$= \lambda.$

As we now have a b.f.p., we proceed according to the rules 3.5.2.

3.6.11

x_1	u_2	u_1	1	
4^*	$-\frac{1}{2}$	$-\frac{1}{2}$	$-\frac{1}{2}$	$= -u_3$
0	$\frac{1}{6}$	$-\frac{1}{6}$	$-\frac{1}{2}$	$= -x_2$
3	$-\frac{7}{6}$	$\frac{1}{6}$	$-\frac{1}{2}$	$= -u_4$
1	$-\frac{1}{6}$	$\frac{1}{6}$	$-\frac{1}{2}$	$= -x_3$
2	$-\frac{2}{3}$	$-\frac{1}{3}$	3	$= \lambda$

3.6.12

	u_3	u_2	u_1	1	
v_1	$\frac{1}{4}$	$-\frac{1}{8}$	$-\frac{1}{8}$	$-\frac{1}{8}$	$= -x_1$
v_2	0	$\frac{1}{6}$	$-\frac{1}{6}$	$-\frac{1}{2}$	$= -x_2$
y_4	$-\frac{3}{4}$	$-\frac{19}{24}$	$\frac{13}{24}$	$-\frac{1}{8}$	$= -u_4$
v_3	$-\frac{1}{4}$	$-\frac{1}{24}$	$\frac{7}{24}$	$-\frac{3}{8}$	$= -x_3$
-1	$-\frac{1}{2}$	$-\frac{5}{12}$	$-\frac{1}{12}$	$\frac{13}{4}$	$= \lambda.$
	$\Vert$	$\Vert$	$\Vert$	$\Vert$	
	y_3	y_2	y_1	μ	

Tableau 3.6.12 gives us the solution: I's optimal strategy is $(\frac{1}{8}, \frac{1}{2}, \frac{3}{8})$. The dual variables, which we had omitted in the intermediate tableaux, tell us that II's optimal strategy is $(\frac{1}{12}, \frac{5}{12}, \frac{1}{2}, 0)$. The value of the game is $\frac{13}{4}$.

Several observations might be made by referring to this

example. The first is that, in pivoting as we did in Tableau 3.6.8, the two variables, u_4 and u_3, were interchanged. But the next step interchanged u_3 and u_1. We could have saved a step by interchanging u_4 and u_1 to begin with—this would have taken us from Tableau 3.6.8 to 3.6.10 in a single pivot step. Thus we see that the rules given in 3.5.1 will not always give the quickest results; modifications may be made which will cut down the number of operations (and hence the time) needed by a significant amount.

A second observation is this: Tableau 3.6.8 does not give us a b.f.p. It does, however, give us a b.d.f.p. A modification of the rules 3.5.1 may be given which will allow us to proceed, not through b.f.p.'s, but through b.d.f.p.'s, until the solution is found. In other words, our method starts with the b.d.f.p. of 3.6.8, but does not make use of the fact that this is a b.d.f.p. Instead, it proceeds to give us a b.f.p., after which it looks for the solution. If, in looking for a b.f.p., we are careful to keep to tableaux which are also b.d.f.p.'s, then it is clear that the first b.f.p. we reach will be the solution.

The third observation is that we need not keep track of the dual variables, y_j and v_i. In fact, each y_j will necessarily be located opposite the corresponding u_j of the maximizing problem; the same holds for the v_i and x_i. Indeed, it is clear that each pivot step will preserve these relative positions.

III.6.4 Example

Maximize $x_1 + x_2$

subject to

$$\begin{aligned} -2x_1 + x_2 &\le -3 \\ x_1 - 2x_2 &\le 4 \\ x_1, x_2 &\ge 0. \end{aligned}$$

Solution: We obtain the tableau:

3.6.13

	x_1	x_2	1	
	-2	1	-3	$= -u_1$
	1	-2^*	4	$= -u_2$
	1	1	0	$= w.$

Pivoting on the starred entry, we obtain the tableaux:

3.6.14

x_1	u_2	1	
$-\frac{7}{4}$*	$\frac{1}{2}$	5	$= -u_1$
$-\frac{1}{2}$	$-\frac{1}{2}$	-2	$= -x_2$
$\frac{3}{2}$	$\frac{1}{2}$	2	$= w$

3.6.15

u_1	u_2	1	
$-\frac{4}{7}$	$-\frac{2}{7}$	$-\frac{20}{7}$	$= -x_1$
$-\frac{2}{7}$	$-\frac{9}{14}$	$-\frac{24}{7}$	$= -x_2$
$\frac{6}{7}$	$\frac{13}{14}$	$\frac{44}{7}$	$= w.$

It is clear from 3.6.15 that the problem is unbounded.

III.7 CONSTRAINED GAMES

The theory of linear programming has many applications other than to the theory of games. While many of these are very interesting in their own right, it is not possible, within the scope of this book, to treat them in any detail. We give here an application which does pertain to games.

Let us consider a game in which not all mixed strategies are permitted. There is generally some practical reason why this should be. Now, we assume that the mixed strategies x and y, respectively, must be chosen from some convex hyperpolyhedron, i.e., from constraint sets determined by linear inequalities and equations.

If the game matrix is $A = (a_{ij})$, then player I's problem is to find

3.7.1 $\max_{x \in X} \left\{ \min_{y \in Y} xAy^t \right\}$

where the two sets, X and Y, are determined by

3.7.2 $xB \leq C$

3.7.3 $x \geq 0$

and

3.7.4 $yE^t \geq F$

3.7.5 $y \geq 0$

respectively. Player II's problem would, similarly, be to find

3.7.6 $\min_{y \in Y} \left\{ \max_{x \in X} xAy^t \right\}.$

Consider then the expression 3.7.1. The expression inside the brackets, clearly, is a function of x. More exactly, it is the value of a linear program whose objective function has coefficients depending on x. By the duality theorems given in III.2 we know that if this program is feasible and bounded (which generally does not depend on x), then the two programs

3.7.7 Minimize $(xA)y^t$

subject to

3.7.8 $yE^t \geq F$

3.7.9 $y \geq 0$

and

3.7.10 Maximize zF^t

subject to

3.7.11 $zE \leq xA$

3.7.12 $z \geq 0$

will have the same value. Thus, player I's problem reduces to the pure maximization problem:

3.7.13 Maximize zF^t

subject to

3.7.14 $zE - xA \leq 0$

3.7.15 $xB \leq C$

3.7.16 $z, x \geq 0.$

This problem, of course, can be solved by the usual linear programming techniques (generally, the simplex algorithm).

In a similar way, it can be seen that player II's problem (3.7.6) reduces to the pure minimization problem

3.7.17 Minimize Cs^t

subject to

3.7.18 $sB^t - yA^t \geq 0$

3.7.19 $yE^t \geq F$

3.7.20 $s, y \geq 0.$

It can be seen that (3.7.17)–(3.7.20) is the dual of (3.7.13)–(3.7.16). Therefore, if both of these programs are feasible the two expressions 3.7.1 and 3.7.6 will be equal, and thus the constrained game will have a saddle point in mixed strategies.

PROBLEMS

1. Give the duals of the following linear programs:

(a) Maximize $x_1 + 3x_2 - x_3$

subject to
$$\begin{aligned} 3x_1 + x_2 &\leq 5 \\ x_1 - 3x_2 + x_3 &\geq -6 \\ x_2 + 3x_3 &\leq 4 \\ x_i &\geq 0 \qquad i = 1, 2, 3 \end{aligned}$$

(b) Minimize $2x_1 + 5x_2 + 6x_3$

subject to
$$\begin{aligned} x_1 + 3x_2 + x_3 &\geq 5 \\ 3x_2 + 2x_3 &\geq 7 \\ x_1 + x_3 &\geq 3 \\ x_i &\geq 0, \qquad i = 1, 2, 3. \end{aligned}$$

2. Show that the program

Minimize $2x_1 - 3x_2 + 4x_3$

subject to
$$\begin{aligned} 2x_2 - x_3 &\geq -2 \\ -2x_1 + 3x_3 &\geq +3 \\ x_1 - 3x_2 &\geq -4 \\ x_i &\geq 0, \qquad i = 1, 2, 3 \end{aligned}$$

has value zero. (Hint: show that it is feasible; then find its dual.)

3. Let $A(x, y)$ be a continuous function of x and y in the unit square $[0, 1] \times [0, 1]$. Let $b(y)$ and $c(x)$ be defined and

continuous on [0, 1]. Show that, if $f(x)$ and $g(y)$ are continuous non-negative functions on [0, 1], such that

$$\int_0^1 A(x, y) f(x)\, dx \leq b(y)$$

and

$$\int_0^1 A(x, y) g(y)\, dy \geq c(x)$$

then

$$\int_0^1 c(x) f(x)\, dx \leq \int_0^1 b(y) g(y)\, dy.$$

4. Let A be a matrix game, and let B be a matrix of the same size as A. Letting $v(A)$ be the value of A, define

$$\frac{\partial v(A)}{\partial B} = \lim_{\alpha \to 0+} \frac{v(A + \alpha B) - v(A)}{\alpha}.$$

Show that

$$\frac{\partial v(A)}{\partial B} = \max_{x \in X^*} \min_{y \in Y^*} x B y^t$$

where X^* and Y^* are the sets of optimal strategies for I and II, respectively, in A.

5. A *flow problem* consists of a system of nodes (vertices), numbered 0, 1, 2, . . . , $n + 1$ connected by arcs, $A_{ij} (i \neq j)$. The nodes numbered 0 and $n + 1$ are distinguished, being called respectively the *source* and the *sink*. The arcs are undirected, hence A_{ij} and A_{ji} are the same. Each arc has a *capacity*, C_{ij}, while each node also has a capacity, C_{ii}. (Some of the arcs A_{ij} may be missing, in which case we say that $C_{ij} = 0$.) A flow is a vector, $x = (x_{ij})$, in which the component x_{ij} represents the amount "flowing" from node i to node j. The flow must, of course, satisfy the obvious constraints

$$x_{ij} \leq C_{ij} \qquad i, j = 1, \ldots, n$$

$$x_{ii} = \sum_{j \neq i} x_{ij} = \sum_{j \neq i} x_{ji} \qquad i = 1, \ldots, n$$

$$x_{00} = \sum_{j=1}^{n+1} x_{0j}$$

$$x_{n+1,n+1} = \sum_{j=0}^{n} x_{j,n+1}$$

The *value* of the flow is the number x_{00}. Show that $x_{00} = x_{n+1,\, n+1}$.

By a *cut* is meant a collection of arcs and nodes which intersects every chain of arcs and nodes from the source to the sink. The value of a cut is equal to the sum of the capacities of the arcs and nodes in the collection. Prove the max-flow min-cut theorem: The value of the maximal flow is equal to the value of the minimal cut.

6. Maximize $2x_1 + 5x_2$

subject to
$$\begin{aligned} x_1 + 3x_2 &\le 7 \\ 2x_1 + x_2 &\le 6 \\ x_1, x_2 &\ge 0. \end{aligned}$$

7. Minimize $3x_1 + 6x_2 - x_3$

subject to
$$\begin{aligned} x_1 + 4x_2 + 5x_3 &\ge 7 \\ 3x_2 + x_3 &\ge 5 \\ 3x_1 \qquad\quad - x_3 &\ge 8 \\ x_1, x_2, x_3 &\ge 0. \end{aligned}$$

8. Maximize $x_1 + 4x_2 - 6x_3$

subject to
$$\begin{aligned} 3x_1 + 2x_2 - x_3 &\le 5 \\ x_1 \qquad\quad + 4x_3 &\le 7 \\ -x_1 + 4x_2 + x_3 &\le 8 \\ x_1, x_2, x_3 &\ge 0. \end{aligned}$$

9. Minimize $x_1 + x_2 + x_3 + x_4$

subject to
$$\begin{aligned} 3x_1 + 2x_2 + x_3 + x_4 &\ge 1 \\ x_2 + x_3 - x_4 &\ge 6 \\ x_1 \qquad\quad + x_3 + 2x_4 &= 8 \\ x_1, x_2, x_3, x_4 &\ge 0. \end{aligned}$$

Find a pair of optimal strategies, and the value, for the following matrix games:

10. $$\begin{pmatrix} 4 & 3 & 1 & 4 \\ 2 & 5 & 6 & 3 \\ 1 & 0 & 7 & 0 \end{pmatrix}.$$

11. $\begin{pmatrix} 0 & 5 & -2 \\ -3 & 0 & 4 \\ 6 & -4 & 0 \end{pmatrix}.$

12. $\begin{pmatrix} 5 & 8 & 3 & 1 & 6 \\ 4 & 2 & 6 & 3 & 5 \\ 2 & 4 & 6 & 4 & 1 \\ 1 & 3 & 2 & 5 & 3 \end{pmatrix}.$

CHAPTER IV

INFINITE GAMES

IV.1 GAMES WITH COUNTABLY MANY STRATEGIES

Thus far we have dealt mainly with finite games: i.e., games in which each player has a finite number of strategies. Let us consider now a generalization to infinite games. We consider first of all games with countably many pure strategies. These will, generally, be labeled with the positive integers. As in the case of finite games, we shall let a_{ij} represent the expected payoff from II to I, assuming that I chooses his i^{th} pure strategy, while II chooses his j^{th} pure strategy.

A mixed strategy for I, in this case, will be a sequence $(x_1, x_2, \ldots)$ satisfying

4.1.1 $$\sum_{i=1}^{\infty} x_i = 1$$

4.1.2 $$x_i \geq 0.$$

A mixed strategy for II will be a sequence $(y_1, y_2, \ldots)$ defined similarly. The payoff function for the mixed strategies (x, y) will be defined as

4.1.3 $$A(x, y) = \sum_{x,y=1}^{\infty} x_i a_{ij} y_j$$

assuming that this series converges absolutely.

Games with countably many strategies exhibit several undesirable properties which are not found among finite games. The difficulties are as follows: first, the series 4.1.3 need not converge, and when this does not happen, it may be that the two iterated sums

4.1.4 $$\sum_{x=1}^{\infty} \sum_{y=1}^{\infty} x_i a_{ij} y_j$$

and

4.1.5 $$\sum_{y=1}^{\infty} \sum_{x=1}^{\infty} x_i a_{ij} y_j$$

will exist and be different. Secondly, the sets of mixed strategies are not compact, and thus maxima and minima will not exist. We give two examples to demonstrate these difficulties; it should be added that there is very little other interest in games with countably many strategies.

IV.1.1 Example. Consider the game with payoff $a_{ij} = \text{sgn}\,(i - j)$. (In essence, this game reduces to the following: each player chooses a number; the one choosing the smaller number pays his opponent one unit.) The game as such is ridiculous; its behavior is even worse.

Indeed, suppose x is a mixed strategy for I. We know that, given any $\varepsilon > 0$, there will exist some N such that

$$\sum_{i=1}^{N-1} x_i > 1 - \varepsilon$$

and so

4.1.6 $$\sum_{i=N}^{\infty} x_i < \varepsilon.$$

If I chooses the mixed strategy x, then let II choose his N^{th} pure strategy. It will be seen that the expected payoff then is

$$\sum a_{iN} x_i < -1 + 2\varepsilon$$

and so

$$\inf_N \sum a_{iN} x_i = -1.$$

But x was arbitrary; hence

4.1.7 $$\sup_x \inf_N \sum a_{iN} x_i = -1.$$

Similarly, it may be seen that

$$4.1.8 \quad \inf_{y} \sup_{N} \sum a_{Nj} y_j = 1$$

and we see that the minimax theorem (even generalized by putting inf and sup instead of min and max) does not hold. Note also that every row and column is dominated.

IV.1.2 Example. Consider the game with payoff $a_{ij} = i - j$. As in Example IV.1.1, the object is to choose a large number; this is further complicated, however, by the fact that the payoff function is not bounded.

Consider now the strategy x, defined by

$$4.1.9 \quad x_i = \begin{cases} \dfrac{1}{2i} & \text{if } i = 2^k,\ k \text{ integral} \\ 0 & \text{otherwise.} \end{cases}$$

It is easily checked that this is indeed a strategy. Now for any j

$$\sum_{i=1}^{\infty} x_i a_{ij} = \sum_{i=1}^{\infty} i x_i - \sum_{i=1}^{\infty} j x_i$$
$$= \sum_{i=1}^{\infty} i x_i - j.$$

Therefore:

$$4.1.10 \quad \sum_{i=1} x_i a_{ij} = +\infty$$

and so it is seen that this mixed strategy, x, gives an infinite expectation for player I against any pure strategy for II. That is, player I can assure himself of an infinite expectation, whatever II does. But the game is symmetric, and it follows that player II can also assure himself of an infinite expectation. Thus we have a pathologic game. Indeed, Example IV.1.1 merely contradicts the minimax theorem; this example seems to contradict common sense.

IV.2 GAMES ON THE SQUARE

An important type of infinite game is that in which each player has a continuum of pure strategies, generally represented as points in the interval [0, 1]. A pure strategy for each player, then, is a real number in this interval. The payoff is a real-valued function $A(x, y)$ defined on the unit square $[0, 1] \times [0, 1]$.

A mixed strategy, as before, is a probability distribution over the set of pure strategies. In this case, a mixed strategy can be represented as a cumulative distribution function: i.e., as a function F, defined on $[0, 1]$, satisfying

4.2.1 $F(0) = 0$

4.2.2 $F(1) = 1$

4.2.3 If $x > x'$, $F(x) \geq F(x')$

4.2.4 If $x \neq 0$, $F(x) = F(x+)$.

If player I uses the pure strategy x, while II uses the mixed strategy G, the expected payoff is the Stieltjes integral

4.2.5 $$E(x, G) = \int_0^1 A(x, y)\, dG(y)$$

but, if II uses the pure strategy y, and I uses the mixed strategy F, the expected payoff is

4.2.6 $$E(F, y) = \int_0^1 A(x, y)\, dF(x).$$

Finally, if I uses F, and II uses G, we have

4.2.7 $$E(F, G) = \int_0^1 \int_0^1 A(x, y)\, dF(x)\, dG(y)$$

assuming, in each case, that these integrals exist. If they exist, of course, we have

4.2.8 $$E(F, G) = \int_0^1 E(F, y)\, dG(y) = \int_0^1 E(x, G)\, dF(x).$$

Optimal Strategies and Value. As with finite games, we can define the two numbers

4.2.9 $$v_{\mathrm{I}} = \sup_F \inf_y E(F, y)$$

and

4.2.10 $$v_{\mathrm{II}} = \inf_G \sup_x E(x, G).$$

Two questions arise now. (1) Will $v_{\mathrm{I}} = v_{\mathrm{II}}$? (2) Can sup inf and inf sup be replaced by max min and min max, respectively? If the answer to both of these questions is in the affirmative, optimal mixed strategies will exist; if these can be found, the game is as well determined as the finite games are. If only the first question can be answered in the affirmative, the game has a value (the common value of v_{I} and v_{II}) but no optimal strategies. It will have ε-optimal strategies, however; i.e., given any $\varepsilon > 0$, there exist mixed strategies, F and G for I and II, respectively, such that

4.2.11 $E(F, y) > v - \varepsilon$

and

4.2.12 $E(x, G) < v + \varepsilon$

for any x or y in $[0, 1]$. Thus, although the game is not as well determined as the finite games, the game seems to show a type of stability.

IV.3 GAMES WITH CONTINUOUS KERNEL

The most obvious candidates for inspection, among games on the square, are those in which the payoff function, $A(x, y)$ (usually called the *kernel*), is continuous. For these, optimal strategies will exist, as we now prove.

IV.3.1 Theorem. If the kernel $A(x, y)$ is a continuous function, the forms sup inf and inf sup may be replaced by max min and min max, respectively.

PROOF: We know that $A(x, y)$ is continuous. Therefore, for any F, the function

$$E(F, y) = \int_0^1 A(x, y)\, dF(x)$$

is a continuous function of y. Since the interval $[0, 1]$ is compact, it follows that $E(F, y)$ will attain a minimum value in that interval. Thus, sup inf may be replaced by sup min.

By the definition of v_{I}, given any n, there exists a distribution F_n such that

$$\min_y E(F_n, y) > v_{\text{I}} - \frac{1}{n}.$$

Now the set of all functions mapping $[0, 1]$ into itself is compact in the topology of pointwise convergence; hence the sequence $(F_1, F_2, \ldots)$ will contain a convergent subsequence. Let the limit of this subsequence be F_0. Since each of the functions F_n satisfies 4.2.1, 4.2.2, and 4.2.3, it is clear that F_0 will also satisfy these three conditions. On the other hand, F_0 need not satisfy 4.2.4, as this is not the type of property which is preserved in the limit. Nevertheless, we define the function $\bar{F}_0$ by

$$4.3.1 \quad \bar{F}_0(x) = \begin{cases} 0 \text{ if } x = 0 \\ F_0(x+) \text{ if } 0 < x < 1 \\ 1 \text{ if } x = 1 \end{cases}$$

and it is easily seen that $\bar{F}_0$ is a strategy. F_0 and $\bar{F}_0$ differ only at their points of discontinuity but, as they are monotone functions, their points of discontinuity form a countable set, and so, for all y,

$$\int_0^1 A(x, y)\, d\bar{F}_0(x) = \int_0^1 A(x, y)\, dF_0(x).$$

The function $A(x, y)$ is continuous and hence uniformly continuous. It follows that, as F_0 is the limit of a subsequence of the F_n,

$$\int_0^1 A(x, y)\, dF_0(x) = \lim_n \int_0^1 A(x, y)\, dF_n(x).$$

But this limit is at least v_{I}, for each value of y. Thus

$$4.3.2 \quad \min_y E(\bar{F}_0, y) \geq v_{\mathrm{I}}$$

and $\bar{F}_0$ gives the desired maximum.

In a similar way, it can be shown that inf sup can be replaced by min max.

IV.3.2 Theorem. If the kernel $A(x, y)$ is continuous, then $v_{\mathrm{I}} = v_{\mathrm{II}}$.

PROOF: For any integer n, consider the $(n + 1) \times (n + 1)$ matrix $A_n = (a_{ij}^n)$ where

$$4.3.3 \quad a_{ij}^n = A\left(\frac{i}{n}, \frac{j}{n}\right) \qquad i, j = 0, 1, \ldots, n.$$

The game with matrix A_n has a value, w_n, and optimal strategies, $r_n = (r_0^n, \ldots, r_n^n)$ and $s_n = (s_0^n, \ldots, s_n^n)$, for I and II respectively.

The function $A(x, y)$ is continuous. Since the square is

compact, it follows that A is uniformly continuous. Thus, given $\varepsilon > 0$, there exists a $\delta > 0$ such that, if

$$\sqrt{(x - x')^2 + (y - y')^2} < \delta$$

then

$$|A(x, y) - A(x', y')| < \varepsilon.$$

Let us take n large enough so that $1/n < \delta$. Form the strategy F_n defined by

4.3.4 $$F_n(x) = \sum_{i=0}^{[nx]} r_i^n$$

(where $[nx]$ is the greatest integer in nx).

For any y, let $j = [ny]$. It is clear that

4.3.5 $$E\left(F_n, \frac{j}{n}\right) = \sum_{i=0}^{n} a_{ij}^n r_i^n > w_n$$

and, since $\left| y - \frac{j}{n} \right| < \delta$,

$$\left| A(x, y) - A\left(x, \frac{j}{n}\right) \right| < \varepsilon$$

and so

$$\left| E(F_n, y) - E\left(F_n, \frac{j}{n}\right) \right| < \varepsilon.$$

Hence, for any y,

$$E(F_n, y) > w_n - \varepsilon$$

and so

4.3.6 $v_{\mathrm{I}} > w_n - \varepsilon.$

In a similar way, we can show that

4.3.7 $v_{\mathrm{II}} < w_n + \varepsilon.$

These two inequalities give us

$$v_{\mathrm{I}} > v_{\mathrm{II}} - 2\varepsilon.$$

But, as $v_{\mathrm{I}} \leq v_{\mathrm{II}}$, and ε is arbitrary, it follows that

4.3.8 $v_{\mathrm{I}} = v_{\mathrm{II}}.$

It should be remarked from the proof of Theorem IV.3.2 first, that

4.3.9 $v = \lim_n w_n$

and second, that the strategies F_n will approximate the optimal strategy as closely as desired. In this sense, the matrix games A_n approximate the continuous game $A(x, y)$. Now, if the kernel is very smooth or flat, it may be that a very small value of n will be sufficient for a good approximation. On the other hand, if the kernel is very irregular, a good approximation will require a larger value of n. The techniques most generally used for solving matrix games (viz., fictitious play and the simplex method) are not generally quick enough for handling games of size, say 100×100. Thus it would be preferable to solve these games by analytic methods; unfortunately, none are available. *Development of such a method is one of the outstanding problems today.* It would also be of interest to develop a method to determine whether the optimal strategy, F, can be a step function: i.e., whether a finite number of pure strategies will suffice, or whether a continuous distribution should be used. The following sections show some progress that has been made in these directions.

IV.4 CONCAVE-CONVEX GAMES

IV.4.1 Definition. A game on the square will be said to be concave-convex if its kernel $A(x, y)$ is concave in x for each value of y and convex in y for each value of x.

Essentially, a concave-convex game must have a saddle-shaped kernel. Because it is saddle shaped, it is to be expected that it will have a saddle point in pure strategies. That this is so, under the additional assumption of continuity, is proved as follows:

IV.4.2 Theorem. Let the concave-convex game $A(x, y)$ be continuous. Then it will have optimal pure strategies.

PROOF: Because the game is continuous, it will have optimal strategies; let these be F and G, for I and II, respectively. Now, let

4.4.1 $$x_0 = \int_0^1 x \, dF(x)$$

4.4.2 $$y_0 = \int_0^1 y \, dG(y).$$

By the concavity of A, given any y, there exists some α such that the function

$$B_y(x) = A(x, y) - \alpha x$$

attains its maximum value (keeping y fixed) at x_0. Thus we have

$$E(F, y) = \int_0^1 (B_y(x) + \alpha x)\, dF(x)$$

$$4.4.3 \quad E(F, y) = \int_0^1 B_y(x)\, dF(x) + \alpha \int_0^1 x\, dF(x).$$

Now, the function B_y has its maximum at x_0, hence the first integral in 4.4.3 is at most equal to $B_y(x_0)$. Thus

$$4.4.4 \quad E(F, y) \leq B_y(x_0) + \alpha x_0 = A(x_0, y)$$

and it follows that x_0 is at least as good as F against any y. Similarly, y_0 is at least as good as G against any x. Thus x_0 and y_0 are optimal pure strategies.

In a sense the proof of IV.4.2 is overly complicated. In fact, Theorem IV.4.2 is concerned with pure strategies; it is hardly to be desired that the proof should involve mixed strategies. We give, therefore, a proof which uses only pure strategies, under the somewhat stronger hypothesis of strict concavity and strict convexity.

IV.4.3 Alternate Proof of IV.4.2 (assuming strict concavity and convexity):

For any value of x there exists a unique value of y (because of strict convexity) which minimizes $A(x, y)$. Let this value of y be called $\varphi(x)$. Thus we have

$$4.4.5 \quad A(x, \varphi(x)) = \min_y A(x, y).$$

Suppose that the function φ is not continuous. Say, then, that φ is discontinuous at x_0, and let $\varphi(x_0) = y_0$. There exists a sequence of numbers, $(x_1, x_2, \ldots)$ such that x_0 is the limit of x_n, but y_0 is not the limit of $\varphi(x_n)$. By compactness, there exists a subsequence of $\{x_n\}$, say $\{x_{n_k}\}$, such that $\varphi(x_{n_k})$ converges, say, to y', where $y' \neq y_0$.

Now,

$$A(x_{n_k}, \varphi(x_{n_k})) < A(x_{n_k}, y_0)$$

and so, taking limits, and using the continuity of A,

$$A(x_0, y') \leq A(x_0, y_0).$$

But y_0 was the *unique* value of y which minimized $A(x_0, y)$. This contradiction proves that φ must be a continuous function.

Similarly, we can define the function $\psi(y)$ to be that value of x which maximizes $A(x, y)$. That is,

$$4.4.6 \quad A(\psi(y), y) = \max_x A(x, y).$$

Consider now the composite function, $\psi \circ \varphi$. It is clearly continuous, mapping $[0, 1]$ into itself. By the Brouwer fixed point theorem, there must exist some $\bar{x}$ such that

$$\bar{x} = \psi \circ \varphi(\bar{x}).$$

If we let $\bar{y} = \varphi(\bar{x})$, this means:

$$4.4.7 \quad \bar{x} = \psi(\bar{y})$$

$$4.4.8 \quad \bar{y} = \varphi(\bar{x}).$$

But this means $\bar{x}$ and $\bar{y}$ are in equilibrium: i.e., they are optimal pure strategies.

IV.4.4 Example. Consider the game with kernel

$$A(x, y) = -2x^2 + y^2 + 3xy - x - 2y.$$

It is seen that $A_{xx} = -4$, and $A_{yy} = 2$, so the game is indeed concave-convex. We see that

$$A_x = -4x + 3y - 1$$

and, setting this equal to zero, we have

$$x = \frac{3y - 1}{4}.$$

This value of x will maximize A; however, it does not always lie in the unit interval, being negative when $y < \frac{1}{3}$. In such cases the maximum is obtained by letting $x = 0$. Thus we have

$$4.4.9 \quad \psi(y) = \begin{cases} 0 & \text{if } y \le \frac{1}{3} \\ \dfrac{3y - 1}{4} & \text{if } y \ge \frac{1}{3}. \end{cases}$$

Similarly we find that

$$A_y = 2y + 3x - 2$$

which will give us

$$4.4.10 \quad \varphi(x) = \begin{cases} \dfrac{2 - 3x}{2} & \text{if } x \leq \frac{2}{3} \\ 0 & \text{if } x \geq \frac{2}{3}. \end{cases}$$

It is then easy to find the optimal strategies and the value:

$$\bar{x} = \tfrac{4}{17}$$
$$\bar{y} = \tfrac{11}{17}$$
$$v = \tfrac{13}{17}.$$

IV.5 GAMES OF TIMING

It was mentioned before that, although continuous games always have optimal strategies, there is no analytic method of computing these. On the other hand, while we cannot be certain that games with discontinuous kernels will have optimal strategies, there are certain cases in which the discontinuities will enable us to find these optimal strategies (if they exist) by analytic methods.

We are interested here in a type of game on the square called a *game of timing*. The prototype of this game would be a game in which each player can act only once, within a given interval of time. The order in which the two players act is most important; this fact will cause a discontinuity along the diagonal $x = y$ of the square.

We consider, then, a game with kernel $A(x, y)$, of the form

$$4.5.1 \quad A(x, y) = \begin{cases} K(x, y) & \text{if } x < y \\ \varphi(x) & \text{if } x = y \\ L(x, y) & \text{if } x > y \end{cases}$$

where the function K is assumed to be defined and continuous on the set $0 \leq x \leq y \leq 1$, L is assumed to be defined and continuous on $0 \leq y \leq x \leq 1$, and φ to be continuous on $[0, 1]$.

There is no guarantee that optimal strategies will exist. However, we can determine certain properties of the optimal strategies, *assuming that they do exist.*

Let F be a mixed strategy for I. For $y \in [0, 1]$ we have

4.5.2 $$E(F, y) = \int_0^y K(x, y)\, dF(x) + \varphi(y)[F(y) - F(y-)] + \int_y^1 L(x, y)\, dF(x).$$

If F is a continuous distribution we can, of course, omit the middle term here and have

4.5.3 $$E(F, y) = \int_0^y K(x, y)\, dF(x) + \int_y^1 L(x, y)\, dF(x).$$

Let us suppose that F and G are optimal strategies for I and II, respectively, and that they are both continuous distributions. By the optimality of F and G, we know that, if y_0 is any point such that

4.5.4 $$G'(y_0) > 0$$

then

4.5.5 $$E(F, y_0) = v$$

where v is the value of the game. Now, if G' is positive at y, it will also be positive for a neighborhood of y_0, and so, for all y close enough to y_0, we will have $E(F, y) = v$. But this means that

4.5.6 $$\frac{\partial E(F, y)}{\partial y} = 0$$

and 4.5.6 can be rewritten in the form

4.5.7 $$[L(y, y) - K(y, y)]F'(y) = \int_0^y K_2(x, y)F'(x)\, dx + \int_y^1 L_2(x, y)F'(x)\, dx$$

(an integral equation in F' which is sometimes reasonably easy to solve).

Suppose, then, that we are given a game with kernel of the form 4.5.1. We have no guarantee that optimal strategies will exist; we don't even know whether these will be continuous, discrete, or partly continuous and partly discrete distributions. It seems reasonable to assume that the optimal strategies, F and G, will be continuous distributions, with derivatives F' and G' which are positive in a certain pair of intervals, (a, b) and (c, d) respectively, and vanish outside these intervals. We then have several relations which must hold among the functions F, G and the numbers a, b, c, d, v. These are:

4.5.8 $\quad E(F, y) = v \quad \text{for } y \in (c, d)$

4.5.9 $\quad E(F, y) \geq v \quad \text{for all } y$

4.5.10 $\quad E(x, G) = v \quad \text{for } x \in (a, b)$

4.5.11 $\quad E(x, G) \leq v \quad \text{for all } x$

4.5.12
$$[L(y, y) - K(y, y)]F'(y) = \int_0^y K_2(x, y)F'(x)\,dx + \int_y^1 L_2(x, y)F'(x)\,dx \qquad \text{for } y \in (c, d)$$

4.5.13
$$[K(x, x) - L(x, x)]G'(x) = \int_0^x L_1(x, y)G'(y)\,dy + \int_x^1 K_1(x, y)G'(y)\,dy \qquad \text{for } x \in (a, b).$$

To these six relations, we must, of course, add the constraints that F and G must be strategies and that $0 \leq a < b \leq 1$, $0 \leq c < d \leq 1$. If the complete system admits a solution, this solution will give us the optimal strategies as well as the value of the game. If there is no solution we conclude that the game either does not have optimal strategies or, if it does, these are not of the type assumed above.

Sometimes the payoff kernel is skew-symmetric: i.e., we will have

4.5.14 $\quad L(x, y) = -K(y, x)$

4.5.15 $\quad \varphi(x) = 0.$

If so, an analysis similar to that in II.6 shows that the value, if it exists, must be zero, and the optimal strategies, if they exist, must be the same for both players. Thus in the formulation of IV.5.3 we will have $F = G$, $a = c$, $b = d$, and $v = 0$. Thus the relations given above will reduce to

4.5.16 $E(F, y) = 0 \quad \text{if } y \in (a, b)$

4.5.17 $E(F, y) \geq 0 \quad \text{for all } y$

4.5.18 $[L(y, y) - K(y, y)]F'(y)$

$$= \int_a^y K_2(x, y)F'(x)\,dx + \int_y^b L_2(x, y)F'(x)\,dx \qquad \text{for } y \in (a, b).$$

This system, together with the usual constraints, will give us the solution of the game, if such a solution exists.

IV.5.1 Example. Consider the following duel. Two men, starting at time $t = 0$, walk toward each other; they will reach each other (if nothing intervenes) at time $t = 1$. Each man has a pistol with exactly one shot, and may fire at any time he wishes. If one hits the other, the duel is immediately over, and the one who fired successfully is the winner. If neither hits the other, the duel is a standoff. If both fire simultaneously and hit each other, the duel is also considered a standoff.

Let us make two assumptions: first, that the accuracy of a shot increases as the players come nearer together, so that, if either player shoots at time t, he has a probability t of hitting his opponent. Secondly, the duel is silent; i.e., a player does not know that his opponent has fired (unless, of course, he is hit).

We compute, now, the kernel. If I chooses time x, and II chooses time y, with $x < y$, then player I has a probability x of hitting his opponent (in which case his payoff is $+1$). If he misses (which has probability $1 - x$) then there is probability y that he will be hit (giving him a payoff of -1). Thus, we have

4.5.19 $K(x, y) = x - y + xy.$

The game is obviously symmetric; we will have

4.5.20 $L(x, y) = x - y - xy$

and

$$\varphi(x) = 0.$$

We also have

4.5.21 $K_2(x, y) = -1 + x$

4.5.22 $L_2(x, y) = -1 - x$

and

4.5.23 $L(y, y) - K(y, y) = -2y^2.$

Assume, now, that the optimal strategy is a continuous distribution F, with positive derivative in an interval (a, b). We will have

4.5.24 $$-2y^2F'(y) = \int_a^y (-1 + x)F'(x)\,dx + \int_y^b (-1 - x)F'(x)\,dx.$$

This integral equation can be transformed into a differential equation by differentiating both sides; it gives us

$$-4yF' - 2y^2F'' = (y - 1)F' + (y + 1)F'$$

or, simplifying,

4.5.25 $yF'' = -3F'$

which has the solution

4.5.26 $F'(y) = ky^{-3}.$

We must now find a, b, and k. Suppose $b < 1$. We know that, for all $y \in (a, b)$, we have

$$E(F, y) = 0.$$

But $E(F, y)$ is continuous in y; it follows that

$$E(F, b) = 0.$$

We have, thus

$$\int_a^b (x - b + bx)\,dF(x) = 0.$$

But, if $b < 1$, this means

$$\int_a^b (x - 1 + x)\,dF(x) < 0$$

and so $E(F, 1) < 0$. This contradicts 4.5.17. Thus we must have

4.5.27 $b = 1.$

We saw that $b = 1$, hence $E(F, 1) = 0$. This gives us

$$k\int_a^1 \frac{2x - 1}{x^3}\,dx = 0$$

which will give us

$$3a^2 - 4a + 1 = 0.$$

This equation has two solutions, $a = 1$ and $a = \frac{1}{3}$. Clearly $a = 1$ is not possible. Thus

4.5.28 $a = \frac{1}{3}$.

Now F is a strategy; hence

$$\int_{1/3}^{1} kx^{-3} = 1$$

and this gives us

4.5.29 $k = \frac{1}{4}$.

This gives us, then, the optimal strategy for either player. It is a continuous distribution, F, defined by

4.5.30 $$F'(x) = \begin{cases} 0 & \text{if } x < \frac{1}{3} \\ \dfrac{1}{4x^3} & \text{if } x > \frac{1}{3}. \end{cases}$$

It may be checked directly that this is the solution.

IV.5.2 Example. Let us consider again the duel given in the previous example, with the sole exception that this time the guns are noisy: i.e., a player knows if his opponent shoots and misses. In such a case, he will naturally hold his fire until time $t = 1$, when he is certain to hit. Therefore, if I chooses x and II chooses y, with $x < y$, we find that I has probability x of winning and probability $1 - x$ of losing. Thus we have

4.5.31 $K(x, y) = 2x - 1$

4.5.32 $L(x, y) = 1 - 2y$

4.5.33 $\varphi(x) = 0.$

We could attempt the same type of analysis as in the previous problem. It is easily seen, however, that this game has a saddle point in pure strategies. In fact we have

$$\begin{aligned} A(\tfrac{1}{2}, y) &= L(x, y) = 1 - 2y > 0 && \text{if } y < \tfrac{1}{2} \\ A(\tfrac{1}{2}, y) &= \varphi(\tfrac{1}{2}) = 0 && \text{if } y = \tfrac{1}{2} \\ A(\tfrac{1}{2}, y) &= K(\tfrac{1}{2}, y) = 0 && \text{if } y > \tfrac{1}{2} \end{aligned}$$

and so $\frac{1}{2}$ is an optimal pure strategy.

IV.6 HIGHER DIMENSIONS

The last four sections have all dealt with games on the square: i.e., games in which the pure strategies for each player form a one-dimensional continuum. It is, of course, true that any set with the cardinality of the continuum can be mapped into the unit interval in a 1–1 manner. Thus, any game in which each player has a set of pure strategies with the cardinality of the continuum can be represented as a game on the square. The difficulty with this, however, is that in doing this many of the properties of the payoff function might be lost. We prefer therefore to maintain the most natural structure possible for the strategy sets.

As before, we will have a function $A(x, y)$, the kernel of the game, defined on the cartesian product, $X \times Y$, of the two sets of pure strategies. A mixed strategy for I will be a measure, μ, defined on X, such that

4.6.1 $\mu(X) = 1$

and, similarly, a mixed strategy for II will be a measure, ν, such that

4.6.2 $\nu(Y) = 1.$

The expected payoff is defined as:

4.6.3 $E(\mu, y) = \int_X A(x, y)\, d\mu(x)$

4.6.4 $E(x, \nu) = \int_Y A(x, y)\, d\nu(y)$

4.6.5 $E(\mu, \nu) = \int_{X \times Y} A(x, y)\, d(\mu \times \nu)$

when these integrals exist. It should be noted, of course, that if 4.6.5 exists, it can be replaced by either of the corresponding iterated integrals.

Values and optimal strategies are defined for these games, exactly as for games on the square. We give the following theorems, easy generalizations of theorems given for games on the square.

IV.6.1 Theorem. If the sets X and Y are compact, and the kernel $A(x, y)$ is continuous, then $v_{\text{I}} = v_{\text{II}}$, and, moreover, optimal mixed strategies will exist.

IV.6.2 Theorem. If the sets X and Y are convex compact subsets of some linear spaces, and the kernel $A(x, y)$ is continuous, concave in x (for each y) and convex in y (for each x), then the game will have a saddle point in pure strategies.

The proofs of IV.6.1 and IV.6.2 are easy generalizations of the proofs of IV.3.1, IV.3.2, and IV.4.2. (Note that these proofs did not use the particular structure of the sets of pure strategies, but only their compactness and convexity.) We will not give them here.

As before, it is necessary to point out that techniques for solving continuous games are not available, but that discontinuities will very often give us the tool to solve such games analytically.

IV.6.3 Example. Two generals, each with an equal number of forces, must fight to take three strategic battlefields. The manner of fighting is such that whichever side has more men at a given field will take that field. It is assumed that the two armies are infinitely divisible, and that the payoff is simply the number of battlefields captured.

The set X will be the set of all ordered triples $x = (x_1, x_2, x_3)$ such that

4.6.1 $$x_1 + x_2 + x_3 = 1$$

4.6.2 $$x_i \geq 0 \qquad i = 1, 2, 3.$$

The set Y is identical; the payoff is

4.6.3 $$A(x, y) = \operatorname{sgn}(x_1 - y_1) + \operatorname{sgn}(x_2 - y_2) + \operatorname{sgn}(x_3 - y_3).$$

Equivalently, each player chooses three non-negative numbers whose sum is 1. A player wins if two of his numbers are larger than the corresponding two numbers chosen by his opponent. There will be a standoff if a pair of corresponding numbers are equal.

We can represent the set X by the equilateral triangle in Figure IV.6.1.

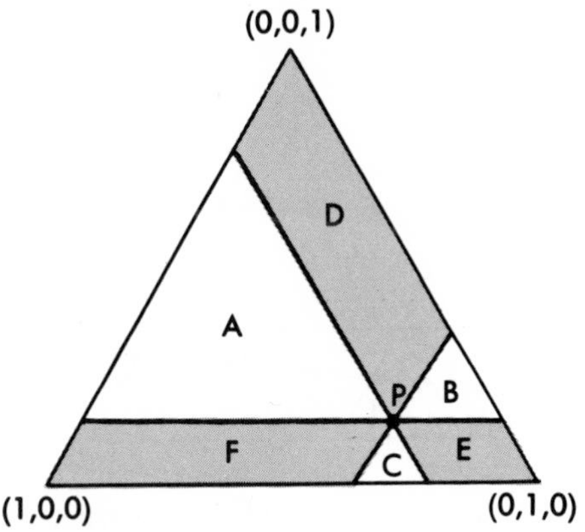

FIGURE IV.6.1

It may be seen that, if a player chooses a point such as P, in the diagram, he will defeat any point in the three areas D, E, and F, but be defeated by any point in the three areas A, B, and C. (There will be a standoff against points on the lines which separate these areas.)

Let us assume that optimal strategies do exist, and that they are continuous distributions which can be represented as the Lebesgue integral of some function, f, which is positive inside some connected set, M, and zero outside it.

Next, suppose that f is positive in the neighborhood of a point, P. If $P' = P + \Delta P$ is any other point in that neighborhood, we know (by the symmetry of the game) that

$$E(\mu, P) = E(\mu, P') = 0.$$

Now, the fact that $E(\mu, P) = 0$ means that

4.6.4 $$\int_{A \cup B \cup C} f \, d\sigma = \tfrac{1}{2}$$

(where σ is Lebesgue measure). Similarly,

4.6.5 $$\int_{A' \cup B' \cup C'} f \, d\sigma = \tfrac{1}{2}$$

where A', B', C' are the sets of points which defeat P'.

It can be seen from Figure IV.6.2 that the difference between the two sets $A \cup B \cup C$ and $A' \cup B' \cup C'$ consists simply of the three strips between the lines L_1, L_2, L_3 through P parallel to the sides of the triangle (the solid lines) and the corresponding lines through P'. If $P = (x_1, x_2, x_3)$ and $\Delta P = (\Delta x_1, \Delta x_2, \Delta x_3)$, we can

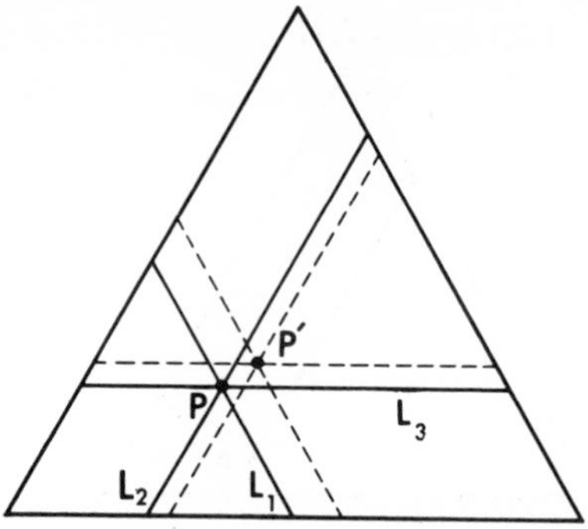

FIGURE IV.6.2

see that, for small ΔP, the difference between the left-hand sides of 4.6.4 and 4.6.5 must be approximately given by

$$4.6.6 \quad \Delta x_1 \int_{L_1} f\,ds + \Delta x_2 \int_{L_2} f\,ds + \Delta x_3 \int_{L_3} f\,ds$$

(where s is Lebesgue linear measure). Now, the expression 4.6.6 must be equal to zero for all values of Δx_1, Δx_2, Δx_3 which satisfy

$$4.6.7 \quad \Delta x_1 + \Delta x_2 + \Delta x_3 = 0.$$

This means that we must have

$$4.6.8 \quad \int_{L_1} f\,ds = \int_{L_2} f\,ds = \int_{L_3} f\,ds = k.$$

We can therefore state that the integral of f must be the same along all lines which are parallel to the sides of the triangle and which intersect M.

We must now determine M. Suppose first that the closure of M does not touch the line $x_1 = 0$. Let us take a point, P, of minimal x_1, in the closure of M. Because it is in the closure of M, Equation 4.6.4 must hold. Consider the point

$$P' = (x_1 - 2\varepsilon, x_2 + \varepsilon, x_3 + \varepsilon).$$

We have, by 4.6.6,

$$\int_{A' \cup B' \cup C'} f\,d\sigma = \tfrac{1}{2} + 2\varepsilon \int_{L_1'} f\,ds - \varepsilon \int_{L_2'} f\,ds - \varepsilon \int_{L_3'} f\,ds.$$

Now, the line L_1' clearly does not intersect the set M, as on it, the first coordinate is smaller than the assumed minimal value of x. On the other hand, at least one of the two lines, L_2' and L_3', must intersect M (if ε is small enough) because M is, by assumption, connected, and not all of M can lie between the two lines L_2 and L_3 (as the area between L_2 and L_3 is precisely the set F). It follows then that

$$\int_{A' \cup B' \cup C'} f \, d\sigma < \tfrac{1}{2}$$

and so $E(\mu, P') < 0$. But this would mean μ is not optimal. Thus *the closure of the set M must touch the three sides of the triangle.*

We know therefore that the minimal values of x_1, x_2, and x_3 in the set M must be zero. To find the maximal values, we note first of all that, if M is connected, every line $x_1 = a$, for a between 0 and the maximal value, r_1, of x_1, intersects M. But this means that the integral of f over M is $r_1 k$. Hence $r_1 = 1/k$. Similarly, the maximal values of x_2 and x_3 (in M) will be $r = 1/k$.

We then find that the set M is inscribed in the hexagon determined by the inequalities

$$0 \leq x_i \leq r \qquad i = 1, 2, 3$$

which is shown in Figure IV.6.3.

Now let P be a point (in the closure of M) with $x_3 = r$. It can be seen that

$$E(\mu, P) = E(\mu, Q)$$

where $Q = (0, 1 - r, r)$, because this expression is constant along the line PQ. In the figure the dotted line through Q divides M into two parts. The part of M which lies above the line consists of points which are defeated by Q; that below the line, of points which defeat Q. Thus the integral of f, over this part of M, must be equal to $\frac{1}{2}$. Now all the lines $x_2 = a$, with a in the interval

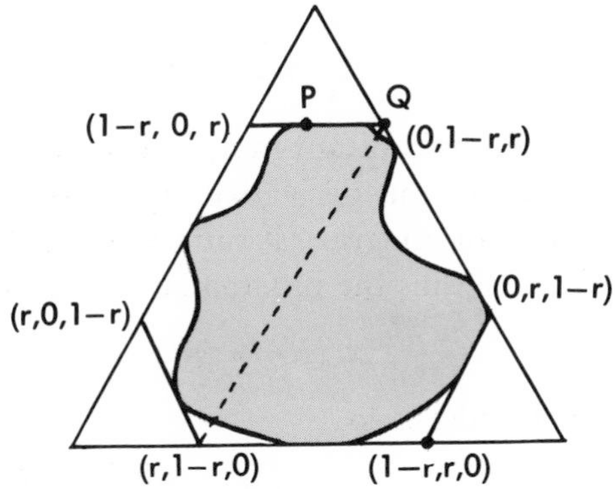

FIGURE IV.6.3

$(0, 1 - r)$, pass through this part; the interval of f here, then, is $k(1 - r)$. Therefore

$$\frac{1 - r}{r} = \tfrac{1}{2}$$

and so

4.6.9 $r = \tfrac{2}{3}$.

Thus we find that M must be a connected set, inscribed in the hexagon $0 \le x_i \le \tfrac{2}{3}$. The function f is zero outside the set M, positive in M, and such that, for every line parallel to one of the sides of the triangle and passing through M, the integral of f is $\tfrac{3}{2}$.

These observations do not determine f or M uniquely; generally, there are many optimal strategies. We might, for example, let M be a circle (the hexagon is clearly regular), and let f be a function only of the distance from the center of the circle. Then if f is chosen so that its integral is constant over all lines in one direction, it will clearly be the same over all lines which intersect M.

Consider, then, a circle, $x^2 + y^2 \le 1$. We want a function $f(R)$ such that, for any $x \in (-1, 1)$, the integral

4.6.10 $$\int_0^{\sqrt{1-x^2}} f(x^2 + y^2)\, dy$$

is constant. If we perform the change of variables

$$y = t\sqrt{1 - x^2}$$

we have

$$R = x^2 + y^2 = x^2 + t^2 - t^2x^2$$

and the integral becomes

$$\int_0^1 \sqrt{1 - x^2} f(x^2 + t^2 - t^2x^2)\, dt.$$

This is constant in x; hence, we differentiate with respect to x, and set the derivative equal to zero. The derivative is, of course, an integral; it suffices to set the integrand equal to zero. We have thus the differential equation

$$xf(R) = 2x(1 - x^2)(1 - t^2)f'(R)$$

which reduces to

$$f(R) = 2(1 - R)f'(R)$$

and has the solution

$$f(R) = \frac{C}{\sqrt{1 - R}} = \frac{C}{\sqrt{1 - r^2}}.$$

We put this back into our problem; we must remember, however, that the radius of the circle we are dealing with is only one third unit; we have, thus,

$$f(x_1, x_2, x_3) = \frac{C}{\sqrt{1 - 9r^2}}$$

where

4.6.11 $r^2 = (x_1 - \tfrac{1}{3})^2 + (x_2 - \tfrac{1}{3})^2 + (x_3 - \tfrac{1}{3})^2.$

The constant C is evaluated by remembering that the integral along any line must be $\tfrac{3}{2}$; this gives us $C = \tfrac{9}{2}$. Thus the optimal strategy is

4.6.12 $f = \dfrac{9}{2\sqrt{1 - 9r^2}}$

for points satisfying $r \leq \tfrac{1}{3}$, and 0 otherwise.

PROBLEMS

1. Let $K(x,y)$ be the kernel of a game over the unit square. Assume K has continuous partial derivatives up to the nth order, and that

$$\frac{\partial^n K}{\partial y^n} \geq 0$$

throughout the unit square. Show that player II has an optimal strategy which uses not more than $n/2$ points (with the stipulation that if an end-point of the interval is used, it shall count only as half a point).

(a) Assume first $\dfrac{\partial^n K}{\partial y^n} > 0$. Assume $F(x)$ is an optimal strategy for I, and show that any strategy optimal against F can use at most $n/2$ points.

(b) Assume now that $\dfrac{\partial^n K}{\partial y^n} \geq 0$. Let $L_\varepsilon(x, y) = K(x, y) + \varepsilon y^n$, where $\varepsilon > 0$. Let G_ε be an optimal strategy for II in L_ε; then, if G_0 is any limit of the strategies G_ε, G_0 will be an optimal strategy for II in K. (Similarly, if F_ε is optimal for I in L_ε, and F_0 is a limit of F_ε as $\varepsilon \to 0$, then F_0 is optimal in K.)

2. Show that, if K is continuous and $K_{yy} \geq 0$ throughout the unit square, then player I has an optimal mixed strategy using at most 2 points.
   (a) Show that II has an optimal pure strategy, y_0.
   (b) If F is an optimal strategy then, for any point x used in F, $K(x, y_0) = v$.
   (c) If I does not have an optimal pure strategy, then he must have two pure strategies, x_1 and x_2, such that $K_y(x_1, y_0) > 0$ and $K_y(x_2, y_0) < 0$.
   (d) I has an optimal mixed strategy using only x_1 and x_2.

3. Let $P(x, y) = \sum_{i=0}^{m} \sum_{j=0}^{n} a_{ij} x^i y^j$ be the kernel of a game over the unit square.
   (a) If the two distributions $F_1(x)$ and $F_2(x)$ have the same moments, i.e., if for $i = 1, \ldots, m$,

$$F_1^{(i)} \equiv \int_0^1 x^i \, dF_1(x) = \int_0^2 x^i \, dF_2(x) \equiv F_2^{(i)}$$

   then F_1 is optimal if and only if F_2 is optimal. Similarly, if $G_1(y)$ and $G_2(y)$ have the same moments, then G_1 is optimal if and only if G_2 is optimal.
   (b) The moments $F^{(i)}$ of any distribution are in the convex hull of the m-dimensional space curve given by the equations $r_i = r^i$.
   (c) Players I and II have optimal strategies using at most m and n points, respectively.
   (d) Give the payoff function, $E(F, G)$ in terms of the moments $F^{(i)}$ and $G^{(j)}$.

   Show that the optimal strategies for the two players can be computed as solutions of a set of algebraic equations.

4. The fact that a game on the square has a continuous, or even rational, kernel does not guarantee that players have optimal strategies using only a finite number of points:
   (a) If $K(x, y)$ is a continuous rational function, and I has an optimal strategy using at most m points, this optimal

strategy can be obtained as the solution of a system of algebraic equations.

(b) If $K(x, y)$ is rational, and v is transcendental, neither player has optimal strategies which use only a finite number of points.

(c) The game with kernel

$$K(x, y) = \frac{(1 + x)(1 + y)(1 - xy)}{(1 + xy)^2}$$

has optimal strategies

$$F(x) = \frac{4}{\pi} \arctan \sqrt{x}$$

$$G(y) = \frac{4}{\pi} \arctan \sqrt{y}$$

and value $4/\pi$.

5. Even a game with a "very regular" payoff kernel need not have a value. Consider the kernel

$$K(x, y) = \begin{cases} -1 & \text{if } x < y < x + \frac{1}{2} \\ 0 & \text{if } x = y \text{ or } y = x + \frac{1}{2} \\ +1 & \text{otherwise.} \end{cases}$$

(a) Whatever $F(x)$ may be, there is some y such that $E(F, y) \leq \frac{1}{3}$. (Distinguish the two cases $F(\frac{1}{2} - 0) \leq \frac{1}{3}$ and $F(\frac{1}{2} - 0) > \frac{1}{3}$.)

(b) Whatever $G(y)$ may be, there is some x such that $E(x, G) \geq \frac{3}{7}$. (Distinguish the three cases: (i) $G(1 - 0) \geq \frac{3}{7}$; (ii) $G(1 - 0) < \frac{3}{7}$ and $G(\frac{1}{2} - 0) < \frac{1}{7}$; (iii) $G(1 - 0) < \frac{3}{7}$ and $G(\frac{1}{2} - 0) \geq \frac{1}{7}$.)

(c) Thus, $v_{\mathrm{I}} \leq \frac{1}{3}$ and $v_{\mathrm{II}} \geq \frac{3}{7}$. Show that in fact the values $\frac{1}{3}$ and $\frac{3}{7}$ are attained by using strategies F^* and G^*, respectively, where F^* uses only 0, $\frac{1}{2}$, and 1, while G^* uses only $\frac{1}{4}$, $\frac{1}{2}$, and 1. Find the probabilities with which these points are used in F^* and G^*.

6. Find the value and optimal strategies of the game with kernel

$$A(x, y) = \begin{cases} 2x - y + xy & \text{if } x < y \\ 0 & \text{if } x = y \\ x - 2y - xy & \text{if } x > y. \end{cases}$$

7. Develop a method for solving a "duel game" in which each player has two bullets instead of one. Assume that the duel is silent so that neither player knows whether the other has shot unless he is hit.

8. Let c_1, c_2, c_3 be positive numbers satisfying the strict triangle inequality $c_i + c_j > c_k$. Consider the following game:

   Player I chooses non-negative numbers (x_1, x_2, x_3) whose sum is 1. Player II similarly chooses (y_1, y_2, y_3). The payoff is $A(x, y) = c_1 \operatorname{sgn}(x_1 - y_1) + c_2 \operatorname{sgn}(x_2 - y_2) + c_3 \operatorname{sgn}(x_3 - y_3)$. Find optimal strategies for this game.

9. Even a game with rational payoff may have a singular solution. Consider the Cantor function, $C(x)$, which satisfies the relations

$$C\left(\frac{x}{3}\right) = \tfrac{1}{2}C(x)$$

$$C(x) + C(1 - x) = 1$$

$$x_1 \geq x_2 \Rightarrow C(x_1) \geq C(x_2).$$

   (a) For any integrable function f,

$$\int_0^1 f(x)\, dC(x) = \int_0^{1/3} f(x)\, dC(x) + \int_{2/3}^1 f(x)\, dC(x).$$

   (b) If f is any continuous function,

$$\int_0^1 \left[2f(x) - f\left(1 - \frac{x}{3}\right) + f\left(\frac{x}{3}\right)\right] dC(x) = 0.$$

   (c) The function

$$K(x, y) = \sum_{n=0}^{\infty} \frac{1}{2^n}\left[2x^n - \left(1 - \frac{x}{3}\right)^n - \left(\frac{x}{3}\right)^n\right] \times \left[2y^n - \left(1 - \frac{y}{3}\right)^n - \left(\frac{y}{3}\right)^n\right]$$

   is continuous and, in fact, rational, for $0 \leq x \leq 1$, $0 \leq y \leq 1$. (Show this by expanding the summand and distributing.) Moreover, $C(x)$ and $C(y)$ are optimal strategies for the two players, giving the value zero.

(d) Let $F(x)$ be any optimal strategy for player I. The function $E(f, y)$ is an analytic function of y. Hence, it either vanishes throughout [0, 1] or has only a finite number of zeros in [0, 1].

(e) If $E(F, y)$ does not vanish throughout [0, 1], then $C(y)$ cannot be optimal for II.

(f) The fact that $E(F, y) = 0$ throughout [0, 1] whenever F is optimal allows us to compute its moments $F^{(i)}$. Hence, any two optimal strategies have the same moments. (By a well-known theorem, this means any two optimal strategies are identical.) Hence C is the unique optimal strategy.

CHAPTER V

MULTI-STAGE GAMES

V.1 BEHAVIORAL STRATEGIES

Let us consider a game with many moves. It may be a game as simple, say, as tic-tac-toe. This game is simple enough so that even a child can learn to master it. Yet suppose we wish to count the number of strategies for the first player. We note (disregarding all symmetries) that he has nine choices for the first move. Then, for any of the eight possible replies, he will have seven choices on his second move. If we consider only the first player's first two moves, we find that he has $9.7^8 = 51{,}883{,}209$ pure strategies. Any attempt to enumerate them, naturally, is out of the question. Even if we consider symmetries, we find that the number of pure strategies for this game is astronomical. And yet the game is quite trivial (in the practical sense of the word, as opposed to chess, which is theoretically trivial but practically very complex).

It is clear, then, that pure strategies leave something to be desired. Let us remember the definition of a pure strategy: it is a function, defined on the collection of a particular player's information sets, assigning to each information set a number between 1 and k (where k is the number of choices at the given information set). Thus if a player has N information sets, and k

choices at each one, the total number of pure strategies is k^N, which can be very large.

Going back to the example of tic-tac-toe we find that no one plays the game by actually considering all possible pure strategies (i.e., all possible sequences of moves from the first to the last). Rather it is played by considering, at each move, all the possible choices *for that move only*, and deciding (from experience or otherwise) which is best.

This, then, is the essence of simplification: take the moves one at a time. It reduces one choice among $k_1 k_2 \cdots k_N$ possible strategies to N choices among the k_i possible moves at each information set. It leads to the following definition:

V.1.1 Definition. A *behavioral strategy* is a collection of N probability distributions, one each over the set of possible choices at each information set.

V.1.2 Example. A player is given a card from a deck of 52 cards; after seeing his card, he has a choice of either *passing* or *betting* a fixed amount. The total number of pure strategies is 2^{52}; thus, the set of mixed strategies will have dimension $2^{52} - 1$. On the other hand, a behavioral strategy simply gives the probability of betting (a number between 0 and 1) with each hand. Thus the dimension of the set of behavioral strategies is 52.

In general, then, the set of behavioral strategies is of much smaller dimension than the set of mixed strategies. On the other hand, it should be pointed out that under certain conditions, not all mixed strategies can be attained by using behavioral strategies, as can be seen by the following example:

V.1.3 Example. In the game with tree in Figure V.1.3.1, we can label player II's pure strategies as LL, LR, RL, RR. A

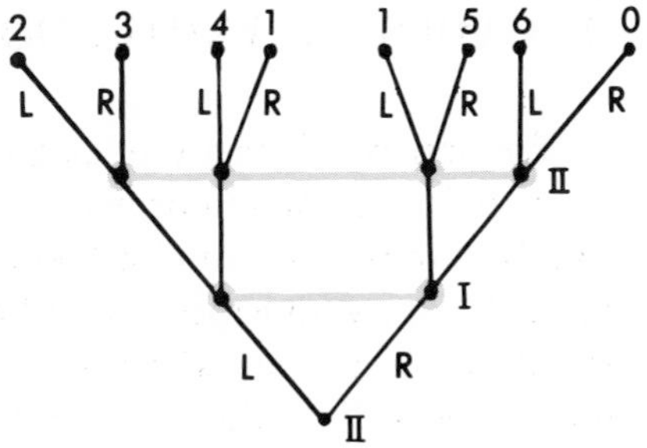

FIGURE V.1.3.1

mixed strategy is a vector (x_1, x_2, x_3, x_4) satisfying the usual constraints; a behavioral strategy is a pair of numbers (y_1, y_2) satisfying only $0 \leq y_i \leq 1$. To the behavioral strategy (y_1, y_2), there corresponds the mixed strategy

5.1.1 $$(y_1 y_2, y_1(1 - y_2), (1 - y_1) y_2, (1 - y_1)(1 - y_2)).$$

Now, the optimal strategy for player II is (see Example II.5.9) the vector $(0, \frac{5}{7}, \frac{2}{7}, 0)$. Clearly, this is not of the form 5.1.1. Hence the game does not admit a solution in terms of behavioral strategies.

In a sense, the difficulty with Example V.1.3 is that player II does not know, at his second move, what he did at his first move. Such a game is said to have *imperfect recall.* This difficulty complicates matters: it is not certain whether all mixed strategies are permitted. In bridge, the two partners are treated as a single player who "forgets" some of his previous choices. As secret arrangements are forbidden, one partner cannot know whether the bid made by his partner was honest or a "psychic" bid, although he may know the probability of such a "psychic" bid.

We shall not enter into these difficulties here. The type of game which we propose to study is very nearly a game of perfect information: after a given number of moves, both players are (simultaneously) given perfect information (which will not be forgotten) so that in a sense the game can be recommenced from the given position. The general pattern will be: first, player I moves; then, player II moves (in ignorance of player I's previous move); next, a random move is made, after which both players are given perfect information. (This pattern may vary, but only slightly.) Each of these cycles will be called a *stage* of the game.

V.2 GAMES OF EXHAUSTION

We now consider a type of game in which each player starts with a finite set of resources. At each stage of the game, one player's resources are diminished by a unit amount. The winner will be the one who wipes out (exhausts) his opponent's resources. Alternatively, at each stage a player might score a point; the winner then will be the one who first achieves a fixed number of points. It is clear that, in the first case, the total resources of the two players are diminished by a unit amount; in the second case, the total number of points is increased by one. Thus these games will always terminate after a certain fixed number of moves.

It is advisable to solve these games by working backward. The general idea is that each stage can be treated as a separate game. When the strategies for this stage are chosen, the payoff will be either a true payoff (in case the multi-stage game terminates) or an obligation to play a subsequent stage of the game.

Since we generally deal with expected values, it follows that we can replace the obligation to play a game by the value of that particular game.

V.2.1 Example. Consider the game with matrix

5.2.1 $$\begin{pmatrix} a_{11} & \Gamma_1 \\ \Gamma_2 & a_{12} \end{pmatrix}$$

where the entries Γ_1 and Γ_2 represent the obligation to play two other games with the respective matrices:

5.2.2 $$\Gamma_1 = \begin{pmatrix} b_{11} & b_{12} \\ b_{21} & b_{22} \end{pmatrix} \qquad \Gamma_2 = \begin{pmatrix} c_{11} & c_{12} \\ c_{21} & c_{22} \end{pmatrix}.$$

If the values of Γ_1 and Γ_2 are v_1 and v_2, respectively, it follows that, in expectation, the prospect of having to play these games is equivalent to their values. Hence we may replace the matrix 5.2.1 with

5.2.3 $$\begin{pmatrix} a_{11} & v_1 \\ v_2 & a_{12} \end{pmatrix}.$$

It is now possible to solve 5.2.3; this will give us the optimal strategies and value for 5.2.1.

For games of exhaustion, then, we start by obtaining solutions to all games in which both players start with only one unit of resources. As the game must terminate in one stage only, it can be solved directly. Using the value of this game, we can then solve all games in which the total resources of both players are three units. These solutions then help us to solve games with four units of resources, then five, and so on.

In general, for games with small amounts of resources (i.e., games which must terminate after a short number of stages) the values and optimal strategies can be obtained directly. For longer games, a recurrence relation can be obtained for the value of each stage. This recurrence relation is generally in the form of a difference equation which may or may not be easy to solve. If the difference equation can be solved, the values for each stage are used to give us the optimal strategies. If the difference equation cannot be solved, it may nevertheless be possible to obtain reasonable approximations of the values and optimal strategies.

V.2.2 Example (The Inspection Game). Player I (the evader) wishes to carry out some forbidden action; there are N time-periods in which this can be done. Player II (the inspector), who would like to prevent this, is allowed to carry out one inspection only, in any one of these time-periods. The payoff is assumed to be 1 if the forbidden action is carried out undetected, -1 if the evader is caught (as he will be if he chooses to act at the same time that the inspector chooses to inspect) and 0 if the evader does not act at all.

In the first time-period (stage) of the game, each player has two choices. Player I can act or not act; player II can inspect or not inspect. If I acts and II inspects, then the game is over and the payoff is -1. If I acts and II does not inspect, the game is over and the payoff is $+1$. If I does not act, and II inspects, then I will be free to act in the next time-period (assuming $N > 1$) and the payoff is also $+1$. If I does not act, and II does not inspect, then we go on to the next stage of the game, which differs only in that there are fewer time-periods left to play. Thus the matrix for the first stage looks like this:

5.2.4 $$\begin{pmatrix} -1 & 1 \\ 1 & \Gamma_{N-1} \end{pmatrix}.$$

This gives us the recursive definition

5.2.5 $$v_N = \text{value} \begin{pmatrix} -1 & 1 \\ 1 & v_{N-1} \end{pmatrix}.$$

Now, it is clear that $v_{N-1} < 1$; hence the game matrix in 5.2.5 does not have a saddle point. We can, therefore, apply 2.5.24 to get the difference equation

5.2.6 $$v_N = \frac{v_{N-1} + 1}{-v_{N-1} + 3}$$

which together with the initial condition

5.2.7 $$v_1 = 0$$

defines v_N. We can solve this equation by the substitution

5.2.8 $$t_N = \frac{1}{v_N - 1}$$

which gives us the new difference equation

5.2.9 $$t_N = t_{N-1} - \tfrac{1}{2}$$

5.2.10 $$t_1 = -1.$$

This equation has the obvious solution

$$t_N = -\frac{n+1}{2}$$

which gives us

5.2.11 $$v_N = \frac{N-1}{N+1}.$$

Thus, 5.2.11 gives us the value of the game at each stage. We can then compute the optimal strategies for each player at each stage. In fact, the game matrix 5.2.3 now becomes

5.2.12 $$\begin{pmatrix} -1 & 1 \\ 1 & \dfrac{N-2}{N} \end{pmatrix}$$

and the equations 2.5.22 and 2.5.23 give us the optimal strategies:

5.2.13 $$x^N = \left(\frac{1}{N+1}, \frac{N}{N+1}\right)$$

for $N \geq 2$.

5.2.14 $$y^N = \left(\frac{1}{N+1}, \frac{N}{N+1}\right)$$

V.2.3 Example (Women and Cats versus Mice and Men). In this fanciful game, team I consists of m_1 women and m_2 cats; team II consists of n_1 mice and n_2 men. At each stage, each team chooses a representative. One of the two representatives chosen is eliminated, according to the following rules: a woman eliminates a man; a man eliminates a cat; a cat eliminates a mouse; and a mouse eliminates a woman. The game continues until one team is reduced to having only one type of player. When a team no longer has any choice, the other team is the obvious winner.

The game matrix, generally, will look like this:

$$\text{5.2.15} \quad \begin{pmatrix} \Gamma(m_1 - 1, m_2; n_1, n_2) & \Gamma(m_1, m_2; n_1, n_2 - 1) \\ \Gamma(m_1, m_2; n_1 - 1, n_2) & \Gamma(m_1, m_2 - 1; n_1, n_2) \end{pmatrix}$$

and considerations similar to those in Example V.2.3 lead to the recursive definition

$$\text{5.2.16} \quad v(m_1, m_2; n_1, n_2)$$
$$= \frac{v(m_1-1, m_2; n_1, n_2)v(m_1, m_2-1; n_1, n_2) - v(m_1, m_2; n_1-1, n_2)v(m_1, m_2; n_1, n_2-1)}{v(m_1-1, m_2; n_1, n_2) + v(m_1, m_2-1; n_1, n_2) - v(m_1, m_2; n_1-1, n_2) - v(m_1, m_2; n_1, n_2-1)}$$

which, together with the boundary conditions

$$\text{5.2.17} \quad v(m_1, m_2; n_1, 0) = v(m_1, m_2; 0, n_2) = +1 \quad \text{if } m_1, m_2 > 0$$

$$\text{5.2.18} \quad v(m_1, 0; n_1, n_2) = v(0, m_2; n_1, n_2) = -1 \quad \text{if } n_1, n_2 > 0$$

defines the value inductively. Unfortunately, this is a non-linear partial difference equation, which is not easy to solve. We can, however, obtain certain results; for instance, if $m_2 = n_1 = n_2 = 1$, we have

$$\text{5.2.19} \quad v(m, 1; 1, 1) = \frac{v(m-1, 1; 1, 1) + 1}{-v(m-1, 1; 1, 1) + 3}$$

and, by symmetry,

$$\text{5.2.20} \quad v(1, 1; 1, 1) = 0.$$

But these equations are exactly those in Example V.2.2 above. Hence

$$\text{5.2.21} \quad v(m, 1; 1, 1) = \frac{m-1}{m+1}$$

and the optimal strategies in such cases are also exactly as in V.2.2.

V.3 STOCHASTIC GAMES

These games are similar to the games treated in Section V.2, but differ in several important respects. Although there are only a finite number of distinct positions, it is possible for the game to revert to a previous position, so that the games can theoretically continue indefinitely. Moreover, there is usually a payoff after each stage of the game, so that, once again, an infinite payoff is theoretically possible. There is, however, a randomization involved which assures that, for all choices of strategies, the probability of infinite play is zero, and the expected payoff is finite.

Specifically, a stochastic game is a set of p "*game elements*" or positions, Γ_k. Each game element is represented by an $m_k \times n_k$ matrix, whose entries are of the form

5.3.1 $$\alpha_{ij}^k = a_{ij}^k + \sum_{l=1}^{p} q_{ij}^{kl} \Gamma_l$$

with

5.3.2 $$q_{ij}^{kl} \geq 0$$

5.3.3 $$\sum_{l=1}^{p} q_{ij}^{kl} < 1.$$

The entry α_{ij}^k, given by 5.3.1, means that if, in the kth game element, player I chooses his i^{th} pure strategy and player II chooses his j^{th} pure strategy, then there will be a payoff of a_{ij}^k units from II to I, plus a probability q_{ij}^{kl} for $l = 1, \ldots, p$ of having to play the lth game element next, and a probability

5.3.4 $$q_{ij}^{k0} = 1 - \sum_{l=1}^{p} q_{ij}^{kl}$$

that play will terminate. Condition 5.3.3 says that, at each stage, there is always a positive probability that play will terminate. Thus the probability of infinite play will be zero, and all expected payoffs are finite.

V.3.1 Definition. A strategy for player I is a collection x^{kt} of m_k-vectors, for $k = 1, \ldots, p$ and all positive integers t satisfying

5.3.5 $$\sum_{i=1}^{m_k} x_i^{kt} = 1$$

5.3.6 $$x_i^{kt} \geq 0.$$

A strategy will be said to be *stationary* if, for all k, the vectors x^{kt} are independent of t.

A strategy for player II is a similar collection of n_k-vectors, y^{kt}.

Briefly, the number x_i^{kt} is the probability that player I will use his i^{th} strategy, assuming that, at the tth stage of the game, he finds himself playing the game element Γ_k. As the element Γ_k may be played several times, player I need not use the same probabilities each time it is played. If, however, he does use the same randomization scheme each time the game element is played, the strategy is said to be stationary. Naturally, a stationary strategy would be preferred from the point of view of simplicity.

Given a pair of strategies, an expected payoff can be calculated for any $k = 1, \ldots, p$ on the assumption that the first stage of the game will be the game element Γ_k. Thus the expected payoff for a pair of strategies can be thought of as a p-vector. As with ordinary matrix games, this will lead to the definition of optimal strategies and a value, the value being a p-vector, $v = (v_1, v_2, \ldots, v_p)$.

It is clear that, if the value vector is to exist, one must be able to replace the game element Γ_k by the value component v_k. It follows that we must have

5.3.7 $$v_k = \text{val}\,(B_k)$$

where B_k is the $m_k \times n_k$ matrix (b_{ij}^k) defined by

5.3.8 $$b_{ij}^k = a_{ij}^k + \sum_{l=1}^{p} q_{ij}^{kl} v_l.$$

This is, of course, an implicit definition only; we must show that there exists exactly one vector $(v_1, \ldots, v_p)$ satisfying 5.3.7 and 5.3.8.

V.3.2 Lemma. Let $A = (a_{ij})$ and $B = (b_{ij})$ be $m \times n$ matrices satisfying

5.3.9 $$a_{ij} < b_{ij} + k \qquad i = 1, \ldots, m; j = 1, \ldots, n$$

for some k. Then val $(A) <$ val $(B) + k$.

PROOF: Let v be the value of B. Let y be an optimal strategy for II in B. Then, for all i,

$$\sum a_{ij} y_j < \sum b_{ij} y_j + k \sum y_j \leq v + k$$

and so y gives a loss-ceiling smaller than $v + k$ in A.

V.3.3 Theorem. There exists exactly one vector $v = (v_1, \ldots, v_p)$ satisfying the relations 5.3.7 and 5.3.8.

PROOF (UNIQUENESS): Suppose that there are two such vectors, v and w. Let k be the component for which $|v_k - w_k|$ is greatest, and, for definiteness, assume $v_k - w_k = c > 0$.

Define the two matrices B_k and $\bar{B}_k$ by

$$b_{ij}^k = a_{ij}^k + \sum q_{ij}^{kl} v_l$$
$$\bar{b}_{ij}^k = a_{ij}^k + \sum q_{ij}^{kl} w_l.$$

It is seen that

$$|b_{ij}^k - \bar{b}_{ij}^k| \leq \sum q_{ij}^{kl} |v_l - w_l| < c$$

and so it follows from Lemma V.3.2 that

$$\text{val}\,(B_k) < \text{val}\,(\bar{B}_k) + c.$$

But since v and w are both assumed to satisfy 5.3.7 and 5.3.8, this means

$$v_k < w_k + c.$$

But we had assumed $v_k - w_k = c$. This contradiction proves uniqueness.

EXISTENCE. We shall construct a sequence of vectors which converges to the desired value vector. We define, inductively,

5.3.10 $v^0 = (0, 0, \ldots, 0)$

5.3.11 $b_{ij}^{kr} = a_{ij} + \sum q_{ij}^{kl} v_l^r \qquad r = 1, 2, \ldots$

5.3.12 $v_k^{r+1} = \text{val}\,(B_k^r) = \text{val}\,(b_{ij}^{kr}).$

We must prove, first, that the sequence of vectors $v^r = (v_1^r, \ldots, v_p^r)$ converges, and, second, that the limit has the desired properties 5.3.7 and 5.3.8. Let

5.3.13 $s = \max\limits_{k,i,j} \left\{\sum\limits_{l=1}^{p} q_{ij}^{kl}\right\}.$

By 5.3.3 (and by finiteness) $s < 1$. If we let

$$t_r = \max_k \{|v_k^{r+1} - v_k^r|\}$$

it is easy to see (by Lemma V.3.2) that $t_r \leq s t_{r-1}$ and so $t_r \leq s^r t_0$. It follows that the sequence of vectors v^r is a Cauchy sequence and so must converge to a limit; call this limit v. Define now

$$w_k = \text{val}\,(B_k) = \text{val}\,(b_{ij}^k)$$

where

$$b_{ij}^k = a_{ij}^k + \sum q_{ij}^{kl} v_l.$$

We shall see that $w_k = v_k$ for all k. In fact, for any $\varepsilon > 0$, we can choose r large enough so that, for all k,

5.3.14 $|v_k^r - v_k| < \varepsilon/2$

and

5.3.15 $|v_k^{r+1} - v_k| < \varepsilon/2.$

From 5.3.14 and Lemma V.3.2, it is easy to see that, for all k, $|v_k^{r+1} - w_k| < \varepsilon/2$; this, together with 5.3.15, means

$$|w_k - v_k| < \varepsilon$$

for all k. But ε was arbitrary; hence $v_k = w_k$.

The second part of the proof of Theorem V.3.3 is a constructive proof, in that it allows us to approximate the values of the game elements Γ_k in a reasonably efficient manner. If we assume that the game will continue as a stochastic game until we have played r times, and then necessarily terminate (if it has not already done so), we obtain a game of exhaustion (the *truncated* game) rather than a stochastic game. If we solve this game of exhaustion by the methods of Section V.2, we obtain the values v^r, as well as optimal strategies for the matrix games B_k^r. The number s, defined by 5.3.13, is such that *the probability that the game continues beyond r stages*, whatever strategies may be employed, *will be at most* s^r. Thus, if r is large enough so that s^r is negligible, we can *approximate the stochastic game by truncating after r stages*. This is precisely what our sequence of vectors, v^r, does. Moreover, the optimal strategies x^{kr} and y^{kr} to the truncated games will converge, in the limit, to *optimal stationary strategies* to the stochastic game.

V.3.4 Example. Players I and II have, together, five units. At each stage of the game, player I chooses heads or tails, and II, in ignorance of I's move, makes a similar choice. If the choices match, II pays I either three units or 1 unit, depending on whether "*H*" or "*T*" was chosen. If the choices do not match, I pays II two units. After each stage, a coin is tossed to determine whether the game will continue or end; moreover, the game will terminate whenever either player is wiped out. We make the additional stipulation that neither player can pay more than he has.

This game can be represented by the four game elements,

Γ_k, where k is the amount held by I at the beginning of a given stage, as follows:

5.3.16 $$\Gamma_1 = \begin{pmatrix} 3 + \frac{1}{2}\Gamma_4 & -1 \\ -1 & 1 + \frac{1}{2}\Gamma_2 \end{pmatrix}$$

5.3.17 $$\Gamma_2 = \begin{pmatrix} 3 & -2 \\ -2 & 1 + \frac{1}{2}\Gamma_3 \end{pmatrix}$$

5.3.18 $$\Gamma_3 = \begin{pmatrix} 2 & -2 + \frac{1}{2}\Gamma_1 \\ -2 + \frac{1}{2}\Gamma_1 & 1 + \frac{1}{2}\Gamma_4 \end{pmatrix}$$

5.3.19 $$\Gamma_4 = \begin{pmatrix} 1 & -2 + \frac{1}{2}\Gamma_2 \\ -2 + \frac{1}{2}\Gamma_2 & 1 \end{pmatrix}.$$

If we use the inductive formulae (5.3:10)–(5.3.12), we obtain, as initial approximations to the values,

$$\begin{aligned} v^0 &= (0, 0, 0, 0) \\ v^1 &= (.33, -.13, -.29, -.5) \\ v^2 &= (.26, -.19, -.29, -.53) \\ v^3 &= (.26, -.19, -.31, -.55) \\ v^4 &= (.26, -.19, -.32, -.55) \end{aligned}$$

and v^4 is the value vector, correct to two decimal places. We can now use v^4 to determine the optimal strategies for each game element. In fact we have

$$B_1 = \begin{pmatrix} 2.72 & -1 \\ -1 & .91 \end{pmatrix}$$

$$B_2 = \begin{pmatrix} 3 & -2 \\ -2 & .84 \end{pmatrix}$$

$$B_3 = \begin{pmatrix} 2 & -1.87 \\ -1.87 & .72 \end{pmatrix}$$

$$B_4 = \begin{pmatrix} 1 & -2.10 \\ -2.10 & 1 \end{pmatrix}$$

and these matrix games have the optimal strategies

$$\begin{aligned} x^1 &= (.34, .66) & y^1 &= (.34, .66) \\ x^2 &= (.38, .62) & y^2 &= (.38, .62) \\ x^3 &= (.40, .60) & y^3 &= (.40, .60) \\ x^4 &= (.50, .50) & y^4 &= (.50, .50) \end{aligned}$$

respectively. These vectors give the optimal (stationary) strategies to the stochastic game.

V.4 RECURSIVE GAMES

Recursive games, while similar to both games of exhaustion and stochastic games, present certain complications which are not found in the others. As with stochastic games, the game elements (positions) may be repeated; as with games of exhaustion, the termination probabilities at a stage may be zero. But these two facts conspire not only to make infinite play possible, but to have a positive probability. To keep values finite, it is, then, generally agreed that there is a payoff only when the game terminates. There may also be a payoff, a_∞, stipulated in case of unending play.

The principal difficulty with these games, as opposed to stochastic games, is that approximation by truncation is not usually feasible. In fact, since infinite play may have positive probability, there is no number r such that the effects of truncation after r steps are negligible. Moreover, since the condition 5.3.3 is replaced by the weaker condition

5.4.1 $$\sum_{l=1}^{p} q_{ij}^{kl} \leq 1$$

it follows that a system of equations similar to 5.3.7 and 5.3.8 need not have a unique solution. Similarly a sequence of vectors v^r, defined as in Theorem V.3.3, need not converge to the true value of the game. We give as an example the recursive game with a single game element,

5.4.2 $$\Gamma = \begin{pmatrix} \Gamma \\ -1 \end{pmatrix}.$$

In this case it is clear that if we let $v^0 \geq -1$, then v^1, v^2, etc., will all equal v^0, while, if we let $v^0 \leq -1$, then v^1, v^2, etc., will all be equal to -1. Hence, while the sequence of values converges, it need not converge to the true value of the game, which is, of course, the larger of the two numbers, a_∞ and -1.

To be entirely specific, a recursive game consists of a finite set of game elements, Γ_k, represented by matrices, A_k, whose entries are of the form

5.4.3 $\alpha_{ij}^k = q_{ij}^{k0} a_{ij}^k + \sum_{l=1}^{p} q_{ij}^{kl} \Gamma_l$

with the q's subject to the constraints

5.4.4 $\sum_{l=0}^{p} q_{ij}^{kl} = 1$

5.4.5 $q_{ij}^{kl} \geq 0.$

If we now take the relations

5.4.6 $v_k = \text{val } (B_k)$

where B_k is the matrix (b_{ij}^k), with

5.4.7 $b_{ij}^k = q_{ij}^{k0} a_{ij}^k + \sum_{l=1}^{p} q_{ij}^{kl} v_l$

we find that these relations will have solutions, even though these are not generally unique. In fact, it is not difficult to see that the function

$$f(v_1, v_2, \ldots, v_p) = (\text{val } (B_1), \ldots, \text{val } (B_p))$$

is continuous (satisfying, indeed, a Lipschitz condition with constant 1). Moreover, if all the v_k are in the interval

$$[\min_{i,j,k} a_{ij}^k, \max_{i,j,k} a_{ij}^k]$$

it is not difficult to see that all the entries b_{ij}^k, and hence the values of the matrices B_k, are also in this interval. By the Brouwer fixed point theorem, there must be a vector v such that $f(v) = v$. Unfortunately, there may be several such vectors, though in many interesting applications these are unique. Generally, the value vector will be that vector which is closest to the number a_∞. (See Everett [V.6] and Milnor and Shapley [V.10] for a more detailed treatment, as well as proofs.) Finally, it should be pointed out that optimal strategies need not exist, but only ε-optimal strategies. As strategies become more nearly optimal, the expected length of the game may increase without limit; thus there will be a discontinuity in the expectation, which will change from v to a_∞ as we approach a limiting strategy.

We give the following example, after Everett [V.6], to show some of these difficulties (this is one of a type of games known as Blotto games, after the protagonist, Colonel Blotto).

V.4.2 Example. Colonel Blotto, with three units, must capture an enemy outpost defended by two units. He must, however, be careful, while he attacks the enemy outpost, that the enemy does not capture his own camp. An attacker needs one more unit than the defending forces to be successful; if the attacking force is not large enough, it simply retreats to its own camp again, and the game recommences on the following day. The payoff is $+1$ if Blotto captures the enemy outpost without losing his own camp, and -1 if the enemy captures Blotto's camp. The payoff for infinite repetition is assumed to be zero.

This recursive game can be represented by a single game element, Γ. The strategies in Γ simply correspond to a division into attacking and defending forces; thus Blotto will have four strategies, corresponding to 0, 1, 2, and 3 attacking units, respectively, while his opponent has three strategies. The matrix is

5.4.8 $$\begin{pmatrix} \Gamma & \Gamma & \Gamma \\ \Gamma & \Gamma & 1 \\ \Gamma & 1 & -1 \\ 1 & -1 & -1 \end{pmatrix}.$$

The value of this game can be seen to be $+1$; Blotto's ε-optimal strategy will be of the form $(0, 1 - \delta - \delta^2, \delta, \delta^2)$. Now the smaller δ is, the larger will be the probability of victory for Blotto, and the larger the expected length of the game will be. Thus it seems patience is most important here. If we let $\delta = 0$, however, then the game might be repeated indefinitely. Thus there is no optimal strategy for Blotto.

Generalizations. We can consider several generalizations of recursive and stochastic games. One possibility would be to permit payments in recursive games even when the game does not terminate. The difficulty then, of course, is that the expected payoff for a pair of strategies need not exist. It might be a divergent series, diverging to $+\infty$ or $-\infty$, or else oscillating. In the first two cases we could say the expectation is infinite, but, in the case of an oscillating series, there is, of course, no expectation.

A second possibility would be to let the game elements, Γ_k, have infinite numbers of pure strategies. Thus the Γ_k may have the form of games on the square, or even more complicated forms. Everett [V.6] shows that these games will also have values and ε-optimal strategies under certain reasonable conditions; the ε-optimal strategies, however, might not be stationary.

V.5 DIFFERENTIAL GAMES

Another possible generalization of stochastic and recursive games is that of games in which the time interval between stages decreases, until, in the limit, a game is reached in which each player must make a move at each moment of time. Because the moves are continuous, it is natural to ask that the game elements change only slightly over small periods of time, i.e., that the game element change continuously. Thus, if a game element is represented as some point in Euclidean space of some dimension, the strategies are generally thought of as defining a differential motion for the point (game element).

More precisely, we can give a definition as follows: the game element is represented by an n-tuple $(x_1, \ldots, x_n)$ of real numbers, known as the *state variables*. At each moment t of time, player I chooses a p-tuple, $\varphi = (\varphi_1, \ldots, \varphi_p)$, of real numbers, subject generally to some constraints usually of the form $a_i \leq \varphi_i \leq b_i$ (where a_i and b_i are constant). Similarly, II chooses a q-tuple, $\psi = (\psi_1, \ldots, \psi_q)$. The vectors φ and ψ are called the *control variables*. The control variables then influence the motion of the state variables, according to a system of differential equations (called the *kinematic equations*)

5.5.1 $\quad \dot{x}_i = f_i(x; \varphi; \psi) \qquad i = 1, \ldots, n$

where the $\dot{x}_i$ should be treated as forward derivatives of the x_i with respect to time.

The differential game continues, according to the kinematic equations, until termination, which is assumed to occur when the state variables reach some closed subset, $\mathscr{C}$, of n-space, whose boundary is called the *terminal surface*. In practical applications, this may mean that player I is close enough to player II to catch him, or that a specified time period has terminated (if a game is to terminate after a specified time, then time is, of course, also a state variable). The payoff then may be of several forms, most common of which are the *terminal* and the *integral* payoff, as well as combinations of these two.

If the game begins at time $t = 0$, and ends at time $t = T$ at the point $(y_1, \ldots, y_n)$, then a terminal payoff is simply a function $G(y_1, \ldots, y_n)$, defined on the *terminal surface* of the game; an integral payoff will be of the form

$$5.5.2 \quad \int_0^T K(x_1, \ldots, x_n)\, dt.$$

The most general type of payoff which we will treat here will have the form of a function, G, plus an integral such as 5.5.2.

The Main Equation. As with discrete multi-stage games, the technique for solving differential games consists in replacing game elements by their values, and then solving recurrence equations for these values. (These equations will now be differential equations.)

Suppose then that values do exist; the value for a game which starts at the point $x = (x_1, \ldots, x_n)$ will be denoted by $V(x_1, \ldots, x_n)$. Let us assume that I chooses the control variable $\bar{\varphi}$, while II chooses the control variable $\bar{\psi}$, at time $t = 0$. In that case, after a very small interval, Δt, of time, we find that the state variables are approximately at the position $x + \Delta x$, where

$$5.5.3 \quad \Delta x_i = f_i(x; \bar{\varphi}; \bar{\psi})\, \Delta t$$

and (if the game has an integral payoff) there will have been a total payoff of approximately

$$5.5.4 \quad K(x_1, \ldots, x_n)\, \Delta t.$$

The game will start again from the point $x + \Delta x$ given by 5.5.3, with a payoff 5.5.4 already effected. If optimal strategies are used from the moment Δt on, the total payoff will be

$$K(x_1, \ldots, x_n)\, \Delta t + V(x + \Delta x).$$

We know, however, that

$$V(x + \Delta x) \cong V(x) + \sum V_i(x)\, \Delta x_i$$

(where V_i is the partial derivative of V with respect to x_i), or

$$V(x + \Delta x) \cong V(x) + \sum_{i=1}^{n} V_i(x) f_i(x; \bar{\varphi}; \bar{\psi})\, \Delta t.$$

Hence, assuming that $\bar{\varphi}$ and $\bar{\psi}$ are optimal choices of the control variables for the time $t = 0$, we have

$$V(x) \cong K(x)\,\Delta t + V(x) + \sum V_i(x) f_i(x; \bar{\varphi}; \bar{\psi})\,\Delta t$$

or, letting $\Delta t \to 0$,

$$\text{5.5.5} \quad K(x) + \sum V_i(x) f_i(x; \bar{\varphi}; \bar{\psi}) = 0$$

or, equivalently,

$$\text{5.5.6} \quad \max_{\varphi}\min_{\psi} \{K(x) + \sum V_i(x) f_i(x; \varphi; \psi)\} = 0.$$

Equation 5.5.5, or the equivalent 5.5.6, is known as the *main equation.* It is generally possible, in Equation 5.5.6, to interchange the order of the two operators, *max* and *min,* although in practice there may be lower-dimensional sets (*singular surfaces*) on which this is not so. Thus pure strategies are generally sufficient; there is need for randomization, usually, only at a finite number of points in any play of the game.

The Path Equations. Once the *main equation* (5.5.5) has been obtained, it is possible (as in games of exhaustion) to work backward from the terminal surface by differential equations (as, before, we worked backward by difference equations). We have, in fact,

$$K + \sum V_i f_i = 0.$$

When we differentiate the left-hand side of this with respect to x_j, we obtain the sum of the terms

$$\text{5.5.7} \quad K_j + \sum_i V_i f_{ij}$$

(where $K_j = \dfrac{\partial K}{\partial x_j}$ and $f_{ij} = \dfrac{\partial f_i}{\partial x_j}$)

$$\text{5.5.8} \quad \sum_i \frac{\partial V_i}{\partial x_j} f_i$$

$$\text{5.5.9} \quad \sum_{k=1}^{p} \frac{\partial}{\partial \varphi_k}(K + \sum_i V_i f_i)\,\frac{\partial \bar{\varphi}_k}{\partial x_j}$$

and

$$\text{5.5.10} \quad \sum_{l=1}^{q} \frac{\partial}{\partial \psi_l}(K + \sum_i V_i f_i)\,\frac{\partial \bar{\psi}_l}{\partial x_j}.$$

Let us consider 5.5.9, supposing that the constraints on the control variables, φ_k, are constant. We know that $\bar{\varphi}_k$ will be either at an interior point, or at an end-point, of its constraint interval. If it is at an interior point, then

$$\frac{\partial}{\partial \varphi_k}(K + \sum V_i f_i) = 0$$

because $\bar{\varphi}$ was chosen to maximize the parenthesis. If on the other hand $\bar{\varphi}_k$ is at an end-point, then (except at points of singularity) it will remain at that end-point, and so

$$\frac{\partial \bar{\varphi}_k}{\partial x_j} = 0.$$

We see thus that the entire term 5.5.9 vanishes; similarly, 5.5.10 will vanish.

Consider next the term 5.5.8. We have

$$\frac{\partial V_i}{\partial x_j} = \frac{\partial^2 V}{\partial x_i \, \partial x_j} = \frac{\partial V_j}{\partial x_i}$$

and so

5.5.11 $$\sum_i \frac{\partial V_i}{\partial x_j} f_i = \sum_i \frac{\partial V_j}{\partial x_i} \cdot \frac{dx_i}{dt} = \frac{dV_j}{dt}.$$

Call the right side of this equation $\dot{V}_j$. If we add this to 5.5.7, and set equal to zero, we obtain the equations

5.5.12 $$\dot{V}_j = -\{K_j(x; \bar{\varphi}; \bar{\psi}) + \sum_i V_i f_{ij}(x; \bar{\varphi}; \bar{\psi})\}$$

which together with the system

5.5.13 $$\dot{x}_j = f_j(x; \bar{\varphi}; \bar{\psi})$$

are called the *path equations* of the differential game. These $2n$ equations, with the value of the function G as terminal conditions, are a formal solution of the game.

It is sometimes easier to use retrograde time $\tau = C - t$ rather than forward time t (since, in fact, we have terminal rather than initial values for the system 5.5.12 and 5.5.13).

V.5.1 Example. Players I and II control the motion of a point in the Euclidean plane, each imparting a velocity whose magnitude depends on the position of the point and whose direction is entirely under the player's control. The velocity of the point is equal to the vector sum of these velocities.

The game will terminate when the point reaches the x-axis; the payoff will be equal to the time needed to complete the game, plus the amount $x_0^2/8$, where x_0 is the abscissa of the point at which play terminates.

If we let $u = y$ and $w = x + y$ be the magnitudes of the velocities controlled by players I and II respectively, we have the kinematic equations:

$$\dot{x} = y \cos \varphi + (x + y) \cos \psi$$
$$\dot{y} = y \sin \varphi + (x + y) \sin \psi$$

and the payoff:

$$\int_0^T dt + x_0^2/8.$$

Thus we have $K = 1$ for all x, y.

It is clear that if we have $u > w$, player I can always extend the game indefinitely. Hence we are interested only in points in the positive quadrant.

The main equation for this game will be

5.5.14 $$y(V_1 \cos \bar{\varphi} + V_2 \sin \bar{\varphi}) + (x + y)(V_1 \cos \bar{\psi} + V_2 \sin \bar{\psi}) = -1.$$

Now to maximize the first term on the left of 5.5.14, we must have

5.5.15 $$\cos \bar{\varphi} = \frac{V_1}{\sqrt{V_1^2 + V_2^2}}$$

5.5.16 $$\sin \bar{\varphi} = \frac{V_2}{\sqrt{V_1^2 + V_2^2}}$$

and to minimize the second term we must have

5.5.17 $$\cos \bar{\psi} = -\cos \bar{\varphi}$$

5.5.18 $$\sin \bar{\psi} = -\sin \bar{\varphi}.$$

If we introduce these values into 5.5.14, and simplify, we obtain

5.5.19 $$\sqrt{V_1^2 + V_2^2} = \frac{1}{x}.$$

We also have

$$f_{11} = \cos \psi$$
$$f_{21} = \sin \psi$$
$$f_{12} = \cos \varphi + \cos \psi$$
$$f_{22} = \sin \varphi + \sin \psi$$

and when we substitute (5.5.15)–(5.5.19) in these, we obtain the path equations

$$\dot{V}_1 = \frac{1}{x}$$
$$\dot{V}_2 = 0$$
$$\dot{x} = -x^2 V_1$$
$$\dot{y} = -x^2 V_2.$$

If, instead of forward time, we use retrograde time $\tau = T - t$, we have the retrograde path equations

$$\mathring{V}_1 = -\frac{1}{x}$$
$$\mathring{V}_2 = 0$$
$$\mathring{x} = x^2 V_1$$
$$\mathring{y} = x^2 V_2$$

where $\mathring{V}_1$ is the derivative of V_1 with respect to τ, etc.

We also have the initial conditions that, for $\tau = 0$,

$$x = x_0; \qquad y = 0$$

$$V_1 = \tfrac{1}{4} x_0; \qquad V_2 = \sqrt{\frac{1}{x_0^2} - \frac{x_0^2}{16}}.$$

These conditions show that we must have $x_0 \leq 2$. This means that none of the paths terminates at a point $x_0 > 2$.

If we differentiate $\mathring{V}_1$ with respect to τ, we obtain

$$\mathring{\mathring{V}}_1 = \frac{1}{x^2} \mathring{x} = V_1$$

and this equation has the solution

$$V_1 = C_1 e^{\tau} + C_2 e^{-\tau}$$

which gives us, in turn

$$x = \frac{1}{C_2e^{-\tau} - C_1e^{\tau}}.$$

If we set $x_0 = a$, we can then introduce the initial conditions that, to solve for C_1 and C_2, we obtain

5.5.20 $$x = \frac{8a}{(4 + a^2)e^{-\tau} + (4 - a^2)e^{\tau}}$$

$$V_1 = \frac{4 + a^2}{8a} e^{-\tau} - \frac{4 - a^2}{8a} e^{\tau}.$$

To find y, we notice that we have

$$\frac{\mathring{y}}{\mathring{x}} = \frac{V_2}{V_1}$$

which (remembering V_2 is constant along any *optimal* path) gives us

$$\frac{dy}{dx} = \frac{V_2(0)}{V_1}.$$

Now $V_2(0)$ is given above, and V_1 can be obtained as a function of x; this gives us

$$\frac{dy}{dx} = \frac{x}{\sqrt{\frac{16a^2}{16 - a^4} - x^2}}$$

which has a solution

$$y = C_3 - \sqrt{\frac{16a^2}{16 - a^4} - x^2}.$$

We solve for C_3 by remembering that, for $y = 0$, $x = a$. We thus have

$$y = \frac{a^3 \pm \sqrt{16a^2 - 16x^2 + a^4x^2}}{\sqrt{16 - a^4}}$$

or, equivalently,

5.5.21 $$x^2 + \left(y - \frac{a^3}{\sqrt{16 - a^4}}\right)^2 = \frac{16a^2}{16 - a^4}$$

i.e., the *optimal path* is a circle with center on the y-axis (see

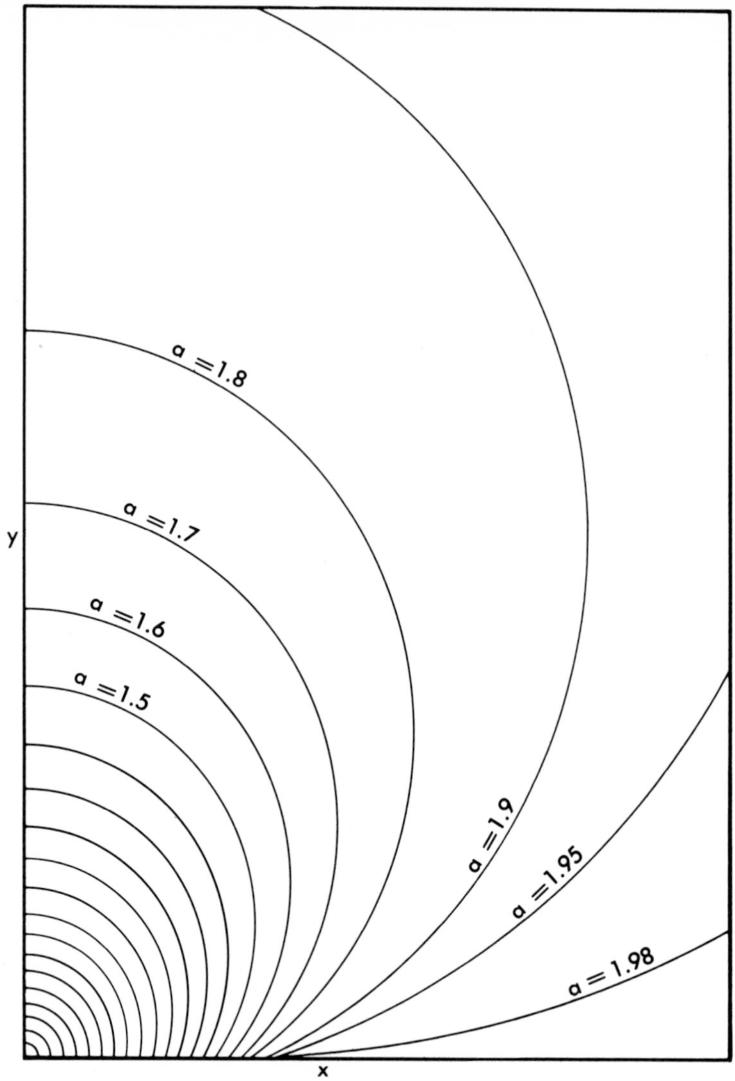

FIGURE V.5.1

Figure V.5.1). The value $V(x, y)$ can be obtained by solving 5.5.21 for a; we then solve 5.5.20 for τ. Then $V(x, y) = \tau + a^2/8$. The optimal strategies are also computable: both players attempt to follow the tangent to the circle 5.5.21. Player I (the maximizer) pushes up (away from the x-axis); player II pushes down (toward the x-axis).

PROBLEMS

1. Show that, for recursive games, the value vector is not the only vector which satisfies the functional equation 5.3.7 and, moreover, the method of successive approximations used for stochastic games need not converge to the value vector.

   Use the recursive game with two elements:

$$\Gamma_1 = (-10) \qquad \Gamma_2 = \begin{pmatrix} +20 & \Gamma_1 \\ \Gamma_1 & +20 \\ \Gamma_2 & \Gamma_2 \end{pmatrix}.$$

2. Extend the results on recursive games to games in which there is a payoff after each play even if the game does not terminate.
   (a) A *trap* is a game element, or set of game elements, such that once a play enters an element of the trap one player can force the play to remain in the trap in such a way as to accumulate payoffs and cause an unbounded expectation. Show that the game with three game elements

$$\Gamma_1 = \begin{pmatrix} \Gamma_2 & 10 & \Gamma_3 \\ -10 & 0 & -10 \\ \Gamma_3 & 10 & \Gamma_2 \end{pmatrix}$$

$$\Gamma_2 = (\Gamma_2 + 1) \qquad \Gamma_3 = (\Gamma_3 - 2)$$

   which has traps does not have a fixed point for the value mapping 5.3.7.
   (b) If a game has all non-negative payoffs, and has no traps, it will have a value.
   (c) Even if a game has no traps, it might have no value if it has both positive and negative payoffs. Give an example. (The value should oscillate under the "best" strategies.)

3. Show that, if time is considered as continuous rather than discrete, a recursive game need not have a value, even if the functional equation 5.3.7 has a unique solution. Consider the game with one game element

$$\Gamma = \begin{pmatrix} 0 & 1 & -1 \\ -1 & 0 & 1 \\ 1 & -1 & \Gamma \end{pmatrix}$$

where the game is played through an interval of time until it terminates. In other words, each player chooses a time at which to act; until that time, he has used his third pure strategy continually.

4. The study of differential games usually involves not only the path equations, 5.5.12, but also a study of so-called singular surfaces. Consider the game played on the half-plane $y \geq 0$, with terminal surface $y = 0$ and terminal payoff

$$G(x^*) = \frac{1}{1 + x^{*2}}.$$

Let the kinematic equations be

$$\dot{x} = \varphi(1 + 2\sqrt{|x|}) + \psi$$
$$\dot{y} = -1$$

where the control variables φ, ψ are restricted to the interval $[0, 1]$. Show that the y-axis is a singular surface in the sense that the optimal paths are a family of curves which *begin* on the y-axis. What should be done at a point on the y-axis (where two optimal paths meet)?

5. It seems quite reasonable to believe that any differential game with integral or continuous terminal payoff should have solutions in fixed strategies, except possibly on a lower-dimensional set (singular surface). Show that this is not so.

Consider the game played on the half-plane $y \geq 0$, with terminal surface $y = 0$, and integral payoff $\int x\, dt$, whose kinematic equations are

$$\dot{x} = (\psi - \varphi)^2$$
$$\dot{y} = -1$$

and, as before, ψ, φ are restricted to the interval $[0, 1]$. Prove that, for any initial point (x_0, y_0), the values in pure strategies satisfy

$$v_{\mathrm{I}} \leq x_0 y_0$$
$$v_{\mathrm{II}} \geq x_0 y_0 + \tfrac{1}{8} y_0^2.$$

Hence the game has no solution in pure strategies for $y > 0$ (nor does it have any optimal paths).

6. A differential game of kind is one which can have only two possible outcomes, say, win and loss (for player I). Thus we can think of the terminal surface $\mathscr{C}$ as divided into two sets, $\mathscr{W}$ and $\mathscr{L}$, which are separated by an $(n-2)$-dimensional manifold, $\mathscr{K}$. Player I tries to bring about termination of the game in $\mathscr{W}$; player II, in $\mathscr{L}$.

In general, the playing space, R^n, will be divided into two parts, called the winning zone (WZ), and losing zone (LZ), such that, from a point in WZ, player I can force termination in $\mathscr{W}$; while from a point in LZ, II can force termination in $\mathscr{L}$. These parts are generally separated by a surface $\mathscr{N}$, which intersects $\mathscr{C}$ along $\mathscr{K}$.

(a) On the assumption that $\mathscr{N}$ is smooth, show that the *normal vector* $(\nu_1, \ldots, \nu_n)$ to $\mathscr{N}$ satisfies the equation

$$\max_{\varphi} \min_{\psi} \sum \nu_i f_i(x, \varphi, \psi) = 0$$

(where ν is oriented toward the WZ). Thus obtain a system of path equations (or retroactive path equations) for these games, similar to 5.5.12.

(b) Consider the following game: Players I and II control the motion of points P and E, respectively, in the upper half-plane of R^2. The two points can move in any direction, at velocities 1 and $w < 1$, respectively. The game terminates with a win for I if ever the distance $\overline{PE}$ is less than d; it terminates with a loss for I if ever E reaches the line $y = 0$.

(c) If we let (x_1, y_1) and (x_2, y_2) be the coordinates of P and E respectively, and let φ and ψ be the control variables, give the kinematic equations for this game; characterize the set $\mathscr{K}$.

(d) Solve this game.

CHAPTER VI

UTILITY THEORY

VI.1 ORDINAL UTILITY

Introduction

In the preceding four chapters we have worked on the supposition that two players have directly opposite interests. Even when the two players form a closed system, with one losing whatever the other one gains, it is not clear that their interests will always be directly opposed. If one player is a rich philanthropist, while the second is poor and deserving, it may be that the first player will prefer to let the second win (up to a certain amount). The fact is that it is not money, but rather the utility represented by the money, that should be considered in such a case. Similarly, the stakes in a game may be something which has no monetary value. Non-monetary (say, sentimental) reasons may make it very valuable for one player, but practically worthless for another. It is this concept of personal value, or personal utility, which must be studied.

Let us consider, then, the fact that a person will prefer certain events to others, and that in other cases, he will be indifferent as to two events. This gives us the two relations, "p" and "i." The domain of these relations will be the set of events. Let us use A, B, C, etc., to denote events.

VI.1.1 Definition. Given any two events, A and B, we say $A \text{ p } B$ if A is preferable to B. We say $A \text{ i } B$ if $A \not\text{p}\, B$ and $B \not\text{p}\, A$.

VI.1.2 Utility Axioms. The relations "p" and "i" satisfy the following axioms:

6.1.2.1 Given any two events, A and B, exactly one of the following must hold:

$$(\alpha) \quad A \text{ p } B$$
$$(\beta) \quad B \text{ p } A$$
$$(\gamma) \quad A \text{ i } B$$

6.1.2.2 $A \text{ i } A$ for all A

6.1.2.3 If $A \text{ i } B$, then $B \text{ i } A$

6.1.2.4 If $A \text{ i } B$ and $B \text{ i } C$, then $A \text{ i } C$

6.1.2.5 If $A \text{ p } B$ and $B \text{ p } C$, then $A \text{ p } C$

6.1.2.6 If $A \text{ p } B$ and $B \text{ i } C$, then $A \text{ p } C$

6.1.2.7 If $A \text{ i } B$ and $B \text{ p } C$, then $A \text{ p } C$.

Axiom 1 is also called the *trichotomy law*. Axioms 2, 3, and 4 mean that i is an equivalence relation. Axiom 5 (together with Axiom 1) means that p is an order relation. Finally, Axioms 6 and 7 are sometimes described by saying that p is transitive over i.

Essentially, the Axioms VI.1.2 represent a weak linear ordering of events, from the most desirable to the least desirable. It is usual to say that, if someone prefers the event A to the event B, then the event A has more utility than B, or the utility of A is greater than that of B.

Unfortunately, while this tells us that the utility of A is greater than that of B, it does not tell us how great this difference in utility is. For certain problems, this represents no difficulty (e.g., if it is merely a question of determining which event an individual will choose). On the other hand, if any risk is involved, it is clear that we must have some idea of the difference in utility between a given pair of events (and not merely which one is preferred by an individual). If, for instance, a person must choose between the event B, and a lottery which will give either the event A or the event C with equal probabilities, and if, moreover, $A \text{ p } B \text{ p } C$, then the problem is to determine whether the possibility of gain (in case A happens) is enough to offset the risk of loss (in case C should occur).

If, now, there existed some commodity (called, perhaps, *utiles*) for which utility were linear (i.e., such that the utility of a certain quantity of utiles were directly proportional to that quantity) there would be no difficulty. We could simply decide the size of the side-payments (in utiles) which would induce our player to abandon A for B, and B for C, respectively, and then act accordingly. Unfortunately, we have seen that no commodity (not even money) behaves in this manner, and thus this idea is deficient. Yet we shall show that such a commodity can be dealt with and considered, just so long as we do not attempt to deal with it as with other commodities which can be bought, sold, transferred, or destroyed.

VI.2 LOTTERIES

We mentioned above that one of the principal cases in which we would like to be able to deal with utiles is that of risk-taking. Now, risk-taking depends essentially on the idea of a lottery.

VI.2.1 Definition. Let A and B be any two events, and let $0 \leq r \leq 1$. Then by $rA + (1 - r)B$ we shall mean the *lottery* which has the two possible outcomes, A and B, with probabilities r and $1 - r$, respectively.

In a similar way, lotteries with three or more possible outcomes may be defined. It should be pointed out that a lottery is also an event. Thus there may be a lottery in which one of the outcomes is another lottery. Moreover, the combination of events by means of lotteries obeys all the usual laws of arithmetic (and linear algebra). We thus have the Axioms

6.2.1 $rA + (1 - r)B = (1 - r)B + rA$

6.2.2 $rA + (1 - r)\{sB + (1 - s)C\}$
$$= rA + (1 - r)sB + (1 - r)(1 - s)C$$

6.2.3 $rA + (1 - r)A = A.$

Axiom 6.2.1, a commutative law, has an obvious meaning. Axioms 6.2.2 and 6.2.3, which resemble the distributive law, state that the manner in which a lottery or sequence of lotteries is held does not matter: only the final probabilities of the possible outcomes matter.

Now, in the lottery $rA + (1 - r)B$, it is clear that it should not make any difference if A is replaced by some C such that $A \text{ i } C$. We have thus the axioms

6.2.4 If $A \text{ i } C$, then, for any r, B,

$$\{rA + (1 - r)B\} \text{ i } \{rC + (1 - r)B\}$$

6.2.5 If $A \text{ p } C$, then, for any $r > 0$, B,

$$\{rA + (1 - r)B\} \text{ p } \{rC + (1 - r)B\}.$$

When we consider the lottery, $rA + (1 - r)B$, we see that, for $r = 1$, the lottery is identical to the event A; while for $r = 0$, the lottery is identical to B. Now it seems reasonable that a very small change in r should cause only a very small change in the utility of the lottery (whatever is meant by this). This, together with the intermediate value theorem for continuous real-valued functions, gives us the axiom:

VI.2.2 Axiom (Continuity Axiom). Let A, B, and C be events such that $A \text{ p } C \text{ p } B$. Then there exists some $r \in [0, 1]$ such that

$$\{rA + (1 - r)B\} \text{ i } C.$$

It should be remarked that, in Axiom VI.2.2, we must actually have $r \in (0, 1)$. In fact, if $r = 0$ or 1, the lottery is equal to B or A, respectively, and by hypothesis $A \text{ p } C \text{ p } B$, so that we cannot have a lottery equivalent (under i) to C in either of these two cases. This can be stated as a theorem:

VI.2.3 Theorem. If $A \text{ p } C \text{ p } B$, and

$$\{rA + (1 - r)B\} \text{ i } C$$

then $0 < r < 1$. Moreover, r is unique.

PROOF: We have seen that r cannot then equal either 0 or 1. To show uniqueness, suppose s is any other number in $(0, 1)$. We may assume $s < r$. We have $0 < r - s < 1 - s$, and so, since

$$B = \left\{\frac{r-s}{1-s}B + \frac{1-r}{1-s}B\right\}$$

and A p B, it follows that

$$\left\{\frac{r-s}{1-s}A + \frac{1-r}{1-s}B\right\} \text{ p } B.$$

Now we have

$$rA + (1-r)B = sA + (1-s)\left\{\frac{r-s}{1-s}A + \frac{1-r}{1-s}B\right\}$$

and thus by 6.2.5

$$\{rA + (1-r)B\} \text{ p } \{sA + (1-s)B\}.$$

The axioms which we have given are now sufficient for the construction of a utility function. Let us consider two cases. The first possibility is that the individual we are dealing with may be indifferent to any choice; i.e., that A i B for any two events A and B. Without asking whether such a person might exist, we point out that this is really a trivial case: all events have the same utility for this individual (who at any rate seems to be a vegetable rather than a person) and he hardly enters the framework of game theory. The second case is dealt with in the proof of the following theorem. (It should be pointed out that the theorem is true in both cases, not just the second.)

VI.2.4 Theorem. There exists a function, u, mapping the set of all events into the real numbers, such that

6.2.6 $u(A) > u(B)$ if and only if A p B

6.2.7 $u(rA + (1-r)B) = ru(A) + (1-r)u(B)$

for any two events A and B, and any $r \in [0, 1]$. Moreover, the function u is unique up to a linear transformation; i.e., if there exists a second function, v, also satisfying 6.2.6 and 6.2.7, then there exist real numbers, $\alpha > 0$, and β, such that, for all A,

6.2.8 $v(A) = \alpha u(A) + \beta$.

Proof (Existence): If, for all A and B, A i B, we can simply let $u(A) = 0$ for any event. Suppose, then, that there exist two events, E_1 and E_0, such that E_1 p E_0. Now, by the Axioms VI.1.2, for any event A, there are five possibilities:

6.2.9 (a) $A \text{ p } E_1$

(b) $A \text{ i } E_1$

(c) $E_1 \text{ p } A \text{ p } E_0$

(d) $A \text{ i } E_0$

(e) $E_0 \text{ p } A$

Let us define, first of all, $u(E_1) = 1$ and $u(E_0) = 0$. We can then define $u(A)$, for any event A, as will be explained. The five possibilities are treated in order.

In case (a), we have $A \text{ p } E_1 \text{ p } E_0$. By the continuity axiom, there exists $r \in (0, 1)$ such that

$$\{rA + (1 - r)E_0\} \text{ i } E_1.$$

We define

6.2.10 (a) $u(A) = 1/r.$

In case (b) we must clearly define

6.2.10 (b) $u(A) = 1.$

In case (c), there exists $s \in (0, 1)$ such that

$$\{sE_1 + (1 - s)E_0\} \text{ i } A.$$

We then define

6.2.10 (c) $u(A) = s.$

In case (d), we will clearly have

6.2.10 (d) $u(A) = 0.$

Finally, in case (e), there exists $t \in (0, 1)$ such that

$$\{tA + (1 - t)E_1\} \text{ i } E_0.$$

In this case, we define

6.2.10 (e) $u(A) = \dfrac{t - 1}{t}.$

We have thus defined a function $u(A)$ for all events A, and must now show that it satisfies 6.2.6 and 6.2.7.

In fact, the proof that u does satisfy these conditions is quite lengthy, depending on whether each of the two events, A and B, lies in case (a), (b), (c), (d), or (e). We shall prove these assuming both are in case (c); the proofs in each of the other 14 cases are quite similar.

Assume, then, that both A and B are in case (c), and that $u(A) = s_1$, $u(B) = s_2$. If, now, $s_1 = s_2$, we see that both A and B are equivalent (under i) to the lottery $s_1E_1 + (1 - s_1)E_0$ and hence $A \text{ i } B$. If, on the other hand, $s_1 > s_2$, it is seen, as in the proof of VI.2.3 that

$$\{s_1E_1 + (1 - s_1)E_0\} \text{ p } \{s_2E_1 + (1 - s_2)E_0\}$$

and so $A \text{ p } B$. Similarly, if $s_2 > s_1$, we see that $B \text{ p } A$. This proves that u satisfies 6.2.6.

To prove 6.2.7, let $r \in (0, 1)$. We have

$$A \text{ i } \{s_1E_1 + (1 - s_1)E_0\}$$
$$B \text{ i } \{s_2E_1 + (1 - s_2)E_0\}$$

and so, by 6.2.4,

$$\{rA + (1 - r)B\} \text{ i } \{r[s_1E_1 + (1 - s_1)E_0] + (1 - r)[s_2E_1 + (1 - s_2)E_0]\}.$$

Hence

$$\{rA + (1 - r)B\} \text{ i } \{[rs_1 + (1 - r)s_2]E_1 + [r(1 - s_1) + (1 - r)(1 - s_2)]E_0\}$$

and so

$$u(rA + (1 - r)B) = rs_1 + (1 - r)s_2$$

or

$$u(rA + (1 - r)B) = ru(A) + (1 - r)u(B).$$

We must, finally, prove that u is unique up to a linear transformation. In fact, let v be any other function satisfying 6.2.6 and 6.2.7. Because $E_1 \text{ p } E_0$, we must have $v(E_1) > v(E_0)$, and so we can define

$$\beta = v(E_0)$$
$$\alpha = v(E_1) - v(E_0) > 0.$$

Now, suppose $E_1 \text{ p } A \text{ p } E_0$. If $u(A) = s$, we know

$$A \text{ i } \{sE_1 + (1 - s)E_0\}$$

and so

$$v(A) = v(sE_1 + (1 - s)E_0)$$
$$v(A) = sv(E_1) + (1 - s)v(E_0)$$
$$v(A) = s(\alpha + \beta) + (1 - s)\beta = s\alpha + \beta$$
$$v(A) = \alpha u(A) + \beta.$$

Similarly, for the other possibilities (a, b, d, e), Equation 6.2.8 may be shown to hold.

We have thus shown the existence of a utility function. The fact that this function is not unique does not detract much from it; in fact, the difference between any two utility functions is only as to the zero and unit of the scale—a difference quite similar to the difference between the Celsius and Fahrenheit temperature scales. By definition, the utility function, u, is linear with lotteries (Equation 6.2.7). The fact that, in a lottery with two outcomes, the first outcome may be given any probability between 0 and 1 means that the range of the utility function is a convex subset of the real line: i.e., an interval. There are 11 types of intervals; one of these, however, is the empty set, while another, consisting only of a single point, clearly applies only to the trivial case mentioned above (of an individual who is indifferent to any choice). This still leaves, however, nine types of intervals, and the question of which of these nine is the true utility space for a given individual remains open.

VI.3 COMMODITY BUNDLES

From an abstract point of view, utilities are assigned to all types of events. This is as it should be, for players differentiate among all types of events. On the other hand, from the economist's point of view, the natural application of utility theory is toward the possession of commodities.

We assume a finite number, say, n, of basic commodities. These commodities are held by different individuals in different quantities. It is natural to use an n-vector, $q = (q_1, \ldots, q_n)$, to denote the amounts of these commodities held by an individual (or group of individuals). We shall call such an n-vector a *commodity bundle*. These commodity bundles are then treated as events: i.e., the event of holding a given bundle. Thus a utility function will be defined on the commodity bundles.

A *caveat* is in order here: we must distinguish between the lottery

$$rq' + (1 - r)q''$$

which gives the bundle q' with probability r and the bundle q''

with probability $1 - r$, and the bundle q defined by

$$q_j = rq'_j + (1 - r)q''_j \qquad j = 1, \ldots, n$$

which is a fixed bundle and not a lottery. For instance, q' could consist of two automobiles without tires, and q'' could consist of ten tires. Letting $r = \frac{1}{2}$, it is clear that the bundle q (one car with five tires) is much preferable, at least for most people, to the lottery $rq' + (1 - r)q''$.

One obvious condition which the utility function must satisfy is monotonicity: if $q' \geq q$, we must have $u(q') \geq u(q)$. It is also sometimes assumed that the function u is continuous, and has continuous first- and second-order partial derivatives (since it is monotone, at least continuity and the first-order partials will exist almost everywhere).

The partial derivatives $\frac{\partial u}{\partial q_j} = u_j$ are called *shadow prices* (they represent, naturally, the price in utiles that would be "fair" for the particular commodity at the given level).

The jth commodity is said to be subject to the *law of diminishing returns* if, for all q,

$$u_{jj} = \frac{\partial^2 u}{\partial q_j^2} \leq 0.$$

Most commodities are assumed to be subject to this law.

The ith commodity is said to be *grossly* substitutable for the jth commodity if

$$u_{ij} = \frac{\partial u_i}{\partial q_j} = \frac{\partial^2 u}{\partial q_j \, \partial q_i} \leq 0$$

i.e., if a decrease in the amount of the jth commodity makes the shadow price for the ith commodity greater. Since we usually have $u_{ji} = u_{ij}$, it follows that *gross substitutability* is a symmetric relation.

The ith and j^{th} commodities are said to be *complementary* if

$$u_{ij} = u_{ji} \geq 0$$

i.e., if an increase in the amount of one of them makes the value of the other greater.

A commodity, say the nth, is said to be *separable* if its utility does not depend on the other commodities: i.e., if there exist two functions, $w = w(q_1, \ldots, q_{n-1})$ and $\varphi = \varphi(q_n)$, such that for all q,

$$u(q_1, \ldots, q_n) = w(q_1, \ldots, q_{n-1}) + \varphi(q_n).$$

A separable commodity is a natural one to use as a medium of exchange. In some cases the function φ is linear; if this holds for two different persons, we say that the nth commodity is *linearly transferable* between the two players. The importance of such a case is that, if the units of utility for the two persons are suitably chosen, a transfer of this commodity from one person to the other will leave the total utility of the two constant. Thus the other $n - 1$ commodities can be divided so as to maximize this total utility; a transfer of the nth commodity (*side payment*) is then used to correct any inequity that this first process may have caused.

VI.4 ABSOLUTE UTILITY

In the field of welfare economics, it is sometimes desired to know whether a certain action "will help individual a more than it hurts individual b." Now this cannot be determined simply by measuring the increase and decrease of utility which this action causes to the two individuals, for we have already pointed out that the units of utility scales are arbitrary and thus cannot be used for interpersonal comparisons. The difficulty is that there is no absolute scale on which to measure utilities for this purpose.

Suppose, however, that the utility spaces of different people are bounded intervals. Then there will be an absolute unit of utility: the length of these intervals. We can normalize all the intervals so that they have 0 and 1 for their upper and lower end-points. It is then natural to compare utilities on these scales.

The problem, then, reduces to the question of whether the utility space of an individual is bounded or not. This is, of course, an open question. Isbell, who favors the bounded interval, suggests the following arguments in its favor:

1. Assume that my utility space is unbounded above. Let A be the event "nothing changes," and let B be the event "I am boiled in oil." As the space is not bounded above, there must be some event C such that:

$$u(C) > 2u(A) - u(B).$$

But this means that:

$$\{\tfrac{1}{2}C + \tfrac{1}{2}B\} \text{ p } A.$$

However, I can conceive of no event C which would make me prefer the lottery $\{\frac{1}{2}C + \frac{1}{2}B\}$ to my present state in life. Hence, my utility space is bounded above.

2. Assume that my utility space is not bounded below. Let A be the event "nothing changes" and let B be the event "I win a million dollars." Now, if the space is not bounded below, there will be some event C such that:

$$A \text{ p } \{.999999B + .000001C\}.$$

But I can conceive of no such event C. Hence my utility space is bounded below.

3. Suppose, moreover, that the utility space is not bounded above. Then there exists a sequence of events, $A_1, A_2, \ldots,$ such that:

$$u(A_n) = 2^n.$$

Then the lottery

$$\sum_{n=1}^{\infty} 2^{-n} A_n$$

will have infinite utility (the Petersburg paradox). Therefore, to avoid this paradox, the utility space must be bounded above. Similarly, it may be argued that the utility space is bounded below.

These are Isbell's arguments for bounded utility; it may be argued that the fact a person cannot conceive of an event C just described simply means his imagination is defective, and that the Petersburg paradox is precisely that—a paradox. The question remains open, naturally. It can only be said that, while things would be simpler with bounded utility scales, we can nevertheless obtain most of the desired results without any recourse to them.

PROBLEMS

1. Complete the proof of Theorem VI.2.2.

2. (Arrow's impossibility proof.) When only ordinal utilities are considered (and no lotteries) there is often no way to determine which action a group of people should take.

Consider a group of m individuals, faced with n alternatives, $A_1, A_2, \ldots, A_n$. By a *profile of individual preferences* we mean a function which assigns to each individual, i, a weak ordering of the alternatives. By a *social welfare function* we mean a function F which assigns an ordering (the "social" ordering) to each profile. The following axioms seem reasonable:

$\mathscr{A}1$: F is defined for all profiles.

$\mathscr{A}2$: Suppose that, for a given profile, A_j is preferred to A_k by the function F. Then A_j will continue to be preferred to A_k if the profile is changed in the following way:
(a) The relative orders of alternatives other than A_j are not changed;
(b) In each of the individual orderings, the position of A_j is improved.

$\mathscr{A}3$: Let ϑ_1 be a subset of $\vartheta = \{A_1, \ldots, A_n\}$. Suppose that a profile is modified in such a way as to leave the relative orderings of the elements of ϑ_1 unchanged. Then the social ordering, F, will also leave the relative ordering of the elements of ϑ_1 unchanged.

$\mathscr{A}4$: For each pair of alternatives, A_j and A_k, there exists a profile such that the social ordering prefers A_j to A_k.

$\mathscr{A}5$: There is no individual, i, such that, for every A_j and A_k, the social ordering prefers A_j to A_k whenever i does so.

Arrow's axioms $\mathscr{A}1$–$\mathscr{A}5$ are inconsistent whenever $n \geq 3$ and $m \geq 2$:

(a) With respect to a given function, F, a coalition S is said to be *decisive* for the ordered pair (A_j, A_k) if, whenever all members of S prefer A_j to A_k, then the social ordering does likewise. A set is decisive if it is decisive for at least one ordered pair (A_j, A_k).
(b) Let V be a minimal decisive set (i.e., V is decisive but no proper subset of V is decisive). Then $V \neq \varnothing$.
(c) Assume V is decisive for (A_j, A_k). Let $i \in V$ and let A_l be any other alternative. Then $\{i\}$ is decisive for (A_j, A_l), and hence, by the minimality of V, $V = \{i\}$.
(d) The set $\{i\}$ is decisive for all pairs, contradicting $\mathscr{A}5$.

CHAPTER VII

TWO-PERSON GENERAL-SUM GAMES

VII.1 BIMATRIX GAMES (NON-COOPERATIVE)

We have so far studied, in general, only zero-sum games. In parlor games, or in situations in which the stakes are small monetary amounts (so that utility will be nearly linear with money), such models are accurate enough. On the other hand, when stakes are more complicated, as often happens in economic situations, it is not generally true that the interests of the two players are exactly opposed; very often, both can gain through cooperation. Such situations are called general-sum games; they include zero-sum games as a special case.

In general, a finite two-person general-sum game can be expressed as a pair of $m \times n$ matrices, $A = (a_{ij})$ and $B = (b_{ij})$, or equivalently, as an $m \times n$ matrix (A, B) each of whose entries is an ordered pair (a_{ij}, b_{ij}). The entries a_{ij} and b_{ij} are the payoffs (in utilities) to the players I and II respectively, assuming they choose, respectively, their i^{th} and j^{th} pure strategies. A game in this form is called a *bimatrix game*.

It is clear that, in many cases, cooperation between the players can work out to both players' advantage. On the other hand, it is possible that, even where this cooperation is mutually beneficial, it is forbidden by the rules of the game (by, e.g., an anti-trust law). We distinguish, therefore, two cases for bimatrix games:

1. The non-cooperative case, in which any type of collusion, such as correlated strategies and side payments, is forbidden.

2. The cooperative case, in which all such cooperation is permitted.

We shall treat, first, the non-cooperative case. As in the case of zero-sum games, we can define mixed strategies for I and II as m- and n-vectors, respectively, with non-negative components whose sum is 1. We define equilibrium pairs in the obvious manner:

VII.1.1 Definition. A pair of mixed strategies (x^*, y^*) for the bimatrix game (A, B) is said to be in equilibrium if, for any other mixed strategies, x and y,

$$xAy^{*t} \leq x^*Ay^{*t}$$

$$x^*By^t \leq x^*By^{*t}.$$

We naturally inquire as to the existence of such pairs. The following theorem answers the question in the affirmative.

VII.1.2 Theorem. Every bimatrix game has at least one equilibrium point.

PROOF: Let x and y be any pair of mixed strategies for the bimatrix game (A, B). We define

$$c_i = \max\{A_{i\cdot}y^t - xAy^t, 0\}$$

$$d_j = \max\{xA_{\cdot j} - xAy^t, 0\}$$

and

$$x_i' = \frac{x_i + c_i}{1 + \sum_k c_k}$$

$$y_j' = \frac{y_j + d_j}{1 + \sum_k d_k}\,.$$

It is clear that the transformation $T(x, y) = (x', y')$ is continuous. Moreover, it is easily seen that both x' and y' are mixed strategies. We now show that $(x', y') = (x, y)$ if and only if (x, y) is an equilibrium pair. In fact, if (x, y) is an equilibrium pair, it is clear that for all i,

$$A_i \cdot y^t \leq xAy^t$$

and so $c_i = 0$. Similarly, $d_j = 0$ for all j. Hence $x' = x$ and $y' = y$.

Suppose, on the other hand, (x, y) is not an equilibrium pair. This means either that there exists some $\bar{x}$ such that $\bar{x}Ay^t > xAy^t$ or that there exists some $\bar{y}$ such that $xB\bar{y}^t > xBy^t$. We shall assume the first case holds; the proof in the second case is identical. Since $\bar{x}Ay^t$ is a weighted average of the terms $A_i \cdot y^t$, it follows that there must be some i for which $A_i \cdot y^t > xAy^t$, and hence some $c_i > 0$. As the c_i's are non-negative, the sum $\sum_k c_k > 0$.

Now, xAy^t is a weighted average (with weights x_i) of the terms $A_i \cdot y^t$. We must, therefore, have $A_i \cdot y^t \leq xAy^t$ for some i such that $x_i > 0$. Now, for this i, we have $c_i = 0$, and so

$$x_i' = \frac{x_i}{1 + \sum_k c_k} < x_i.$$

and so $x' \neq x$.

In the second case we show that $y' \neq y$. Hence $(x', y') = (x, y)$ if and only if (x, y) is in equilibrium.

Now, the set of all strategy pairs is a closed, bounded, convex set, and hence the *Brouwer fixed point theorem* holds. As the transformation $T(x, y) = (x', y')$ is continuous, it must have a fixed point. This fixed point will be an equilibrium pair.

We may remark that the proof of Theorem VII.1.2 can easily be generalized to equilibrium n-tuples for finite n-person games. Let us note also that the proof is an existence proof and gives us no method of finding equilibrium pairs.

The problem of finding equilibrium pairs to bimatrix games has been approached from different sides, and some success has been obtained. The reader is referred to the bibliography for details and methods. Rather than give these methods, we prefer to discuss the difficulties with the notion of equilibrium pairs—difficulties which are most apparent when compared with the parallel notion of optimal strategies for zero-sum (matrix) games.

It has been pointed out (Theorem II.1.2) that, for zero-sum games, equilibrium pairs were both interchangeable and equivalent, in the sense that, if (x, y) and (x', y') are equilibrium pairs for the matrix game A, then so are (x, y') and (x', y), and, moreover, $xAy^t = x'Ay'^t$. This effectively meant that the property of belonging to an equilibrium pair is intrinsic to the vector x (not depending on the vector y, which is in equilibrium with it), and so we consider optimal strategies rather than equilibrium pairs. We give now an example to show that this is not so for general-sum games.

VII.1.3 Example (The Battle of the Sexes).
Consider the bimatrix game

$$\begin{pmatrix} (4, 1) & (0, 0) \\ (0, 0) & (1, 4) \end{pmatrix}.$$

It is obvious that the pure strategies $x = (1, 0)$ and $y = (1, 0)$ are an equilibrium pair; so are $x' = (0, 1)$ and $y' = (0, 1)$. On the other hand, (x, y') and (x', y) are not equilibrium pairs. Moreover, the payoffs for the two equilibrium pairs (x, y) and (x', y') are distinct; (x, y) will be preferred by I, whereas II will prefer (x', y'). Thus it is not clear that these equilibrium pairs are entirely stable; even if I knows that II will use the pure strategy y', he may insist on using x rather than x', hoping that this will induce II to switch to y. In general, it is difficult to tell what will happen. (It should be noticed that the mixed strategies $x'' = (\frac{4}{5}, \frac{1}{5})$ and $y'' = (\frac{1}{5}, \frac{4}{5})$ are also an equilibrium pair.)

Even when there is only one equilibrium pair (as is often the case), it is not clear that this equilibrium pair is exactly what we want:

VII.1.4 Example (The Prisoner's Dilemma).
Consider the game

$$\begin{pmatrix} (5, 5) & (0, 10) \\ (10, 0) & (1, 1) \end{pmatrix}.$$

In this game, it is easy to see that the second row dominates the first row, while the second column dominates the first column (if we adapt the definition of domination, given above for zero-sum games, in the obvious manner). Hence the only equilibrium pair is given by the second pure strategy of each player. This gives the payoff vector (1, 1). But, if both players play "wrong": i.e., choose the first pure strategy, the result (5, 5) is much better for both. The trouble is that each can gain by double-crossing the other.

VII.2 THE BARGAINING PROBLEM

We consider now the case of games in which cooperation between the two players is allowed. This means that binding contracts can be made, that correlated mixed strategies are allowed, and that utility can be transferred from one player to the other (though not always linearly).

There is, generally, a set of outcomes which can be obtained by the two players by acting together. If we choose a pair of utility functions for the two players, this set can be mapped into a subset of two-dimensional Euclidean space, R_2. Its image under this mapping will be closed and bounded above (at least, the sum of the coordinates will be bounded above). Moreover, since lotteries are permitted (by means of correlated mixed strategies) and utility is linear with lotteries, this image will be convex. The problem, then, is to choose a point from this set which will satisfy both players.

Given a two-person general-sum game, then, there is a certain subset S, of R_2, called the *feasible set*. It is feasible in the sense that, given any $(u, v) \in S$, it is possible for the two players, acting together, to obtain the utilities u and v respectively. Generally speaking, however, we find that the more one player gets, the less the other player will be able to get (though this need not always be so). Now, how much will one player be willing to give the other? How little will he be willing to accept, as the price of his cooperation?

Though it is of course impossible to determine how a person will act (in general, there are many personality differences to be taken into account), we can nevertheless set a minimum to the amount that a player will accept for himself. This is the amount that he can obtain by unilateral action, whatever the other player does. This is, of course, the maximin value of the game for that player. Let us call these two values u^* and v^*. Thus

7.2.1 $$u^* = \max_x \min_y xAy^t$$

7.2.2 $$v^* = \max_y \min_x xBy^t$$

(where x and y are taken over the sets of all mixed strategies) if the game is a bimatrix game with matrices (A, B).

We assume, then, that we are given a set, S, together with maximin values (u^*, v^*). We want a rule which will assign, to such a triple (S, u^*, v^*), a "bargaining solution":

$$\varphi(S, u^*, v^*) = (\bar{u}, \bar{v}).$$

We ask, naturally, how such a function, φ, is to be defined. While it is important to repeat that the outcome in any particular case will depend on the personalities and bargaining abilities of the two players, the following axioms seem reasonable conditions to lay on any such function. (These axioms are those of John Nash.)

VII.2.1 N1 (Individual rationality). $(\bar{u}, \bar{v}) \geq (u^*, v^*)$.

N2 (Feasibility). $(\bar{u}, \bar{v}) \in S$.

N3 (Pareto optimality). If $(u, v) \in S$, and $(u, v) \geq (\bar{u}, \bar{v})$, then $(u, v) = (\bar{u}, \bar{v})$.

N4 (Independence of irrelevant alternatives). If $(\bar{u}, \bar{v}) \in T \subset S$, and $(\bar{u}, \bar{v}) = \varphi(S, u^*, v^*)$, then $(\bar{u}, \bar{v}) = \varphi(T, u^*, v^*)$.

N5 (Independence of linear transformations). Let T be obtained from S by the linear transformation

$$u' = \alpha_1 u + \beta_1$$
$$v' = \alpha_2 v + \beta_2.$$

Then, if $\varphi(S, u^*, v^*) = (\bar{u}, \bar{v})$, we must have

$$\varphi(T, \alpha_1 u^* + \beta_1, \alpha_2 v^* + \beta_2) = (\alpha_1 \bar{u} + \beta_1, \alpha_2 \bar{v} + \beta_2).$$

N6 (Symmetry). Suppose S is such that

$$(u, v) \in S \leftrightarrow (v, u) \in S.$$

Suppose also $u^* = v^*$, and $\varphi(S, u^*, v^*) = (\bar{u}, \bar{v})$. Then $\bar{u} = \bar{v}$.

Of these five axioms, N1, N2, and N3 are obvious and need no justification. N4 states that, if a point $(\bar{u}, \bar{v})$ is the solution to a bargaining problem, and then the feasible set is enlarged, the solution to the new problem will either be $(\bar{u}, \bar{v})$ itself, or one of the new points in the set, not a point in the old, smaller set. As such (and, also, in other contexts) it has been open to criticism. N5 is natural enough if we assume that any utility function is as good as any other. It is open to criticism if absolute utility (VI.4) is introduced. Finally, N6 is quite acceptable if the bargaining is between two equal entities; it may not be so acceptable if the bargaining is between unequal entities, e.g., between one person and an entire community.

Several other axioms might be suggested for a bargaining function; an example would be

N7 (Monotonicity). If $T \subset S$, then

$$\varphi(T, x^*, y^*) \leq \varphi(S, x^*, y^*).$$

Unfortunately, N7 is not compatible with N2 and N3. Because it is difficult to quarrel with either of these, we conclude that N7 should be discarded (though someone might claim N7 is not very different from N4). In general, we need consider no further axioms because of the following remarkable theorem:

VII.2.2 Theorem. There is a unique function, φ, defined on all bargaining problems (S, x^*, y^*) satisfying Axioms N1–N6. In preparing the proof of this theorem, we give the following lemmata:

VII.2.3 Lemma. If there are any points $(u, v) \in S$ such that $u > u^*$, $v > v^*$, then there is a unique point $(\bar{u}, \bar{v})$ which maximizes the function

$$g(u, v) = (u - u^*)(v - v^*)$$

over that subset of S for which $u \geq u^*$.

PROOF: By hypothesis, this subset of S is compact. As g is continuous, it must have a maximum over this set. By hypothesis also, this maximum, M, will be positive. Suppose, then, that there are two points (u', v') and (u'', v'') which maximize $g(u, v)$. As $M > 0$, we cannot have $u' = u''$ as this would imply $v' = v''$. Suppose that $u' < u''$; this will mean $v' > v''$.

As S is convex, $(\hat{u}, \hat{v}) \in S$ where $\hat{u} = (u' + u'')/2$, $\hat{v} = (v' + v'')/2$. Now

$$\begin{aligned} g(\hat{u}, \hat{v}) &= \frac{(u' - u^*) + (u'' - u^*)}{2} \cdot \frac{(v' - v^*) + (v'' - v^*)}{2} \\ &= \frac{(u' - u^*)(v' - v^*)}{2} + \frac{(u'' - u^*)(v'' - v^*)}{2} \\ &\quad + \frac{(u' - u'')(v'' - v')}{4} \end{aligned}$$

Now each of the first two terms in this last expression is equal to $M/2$. The third term, however, is positive. But this means $g(\hat{u}, \hat{v}) > M$, which contradicts the maximality of M. Hence the point $(\bar{u}, \bar{v})$ which maximizes g is unique.

VII.2.4 Lemma. Let S, (u^*, v^*) and $(\bar{u}, \bar{v})$ be as in Lemma VII.2.3 above. Let

$$h(u, v) = (\bar{v} - v^*)u + (\bar{u} - u^*)v$$

Then, if $(u, v) \in S$, the inequality $h(u, v) \leq h(\bar{u}, \bar{v})$ will hold.

PROOF: Suppose $(u, v) \in S$, with $h(u, v) > h(\bar{u}, \bar{v})$. Let $0 < \varepsilon < 1$. By the convexity of S, $(u', v') \in S$, where $u' = \bar{u} + \varepsilon(u - \bar{u})$ and $v' = \bar{v} + \varepsilon(v - \bar{v})$. By the linearity of h, $h(u - \bar{u}, v - \bar{v}) > 0$. Now

$$g(u', v') = g(\bar{u}, \bar{v}) + \varepsilon h(u - \bar{u}, v - \bar{v}) + \varepsilon^2(u - \bar{u})(v - \bar{v}).$$

Letting ε approach zero, the last term becomes negligible. This means that $g(u', v') > g(\bar{u}, \bar{v})$. But this contradicts the maximality of $g(\bar{u}, \bar{v})$.

Lemma VII.2.4 says in effect that the line through $(\bar{u}, \bar{v})$, whose slope is the negative of the line joining $(\bar{u}, \bar{v})$ to (u^*, v^*), is a support for S: i.e., S lies entirely on or below this line.

We can now prove Theorem VII.2.2. We shall in fact show that, under the hypothesis of Lemma VII.2.3, the point $(\bar{u}, \bar{v})$ which maximizes $g(u, v)$ must be the solution to the bargaining problem. If this hypothesis does not hold, the problem is much simpler.

PROOF OF VII.2.2: Assume the hypothesis of Lemma VII.2.3 holds. Then the point $(\bar{u}, \bar{v})$ which maximizes $g(u, v)$ is well defined. It clearly satisfies Axioms N1 and N2 by construction. It satisfies N3 for, if $(u, v) \geq (\bar{u}, \bar{v})$, but $(u, v) \neq (\bar{u}, \bar{v})$, then $g(u, v) > g(\bar{u}, \bar{v})$. It satisfies N4 since, if it maximizes $g(u, v)$ over S, it will certainly maximize it also over the smaller set T. It must satisfy N5, for, if we set $u' = \alpha_1 u + \beta_1$ and $v' = \alpha_2 v + \beta_2$, then

$$\begin{aligned} g'(u', v') &= [u' - (\alpha_1 u^* + \beta_1)][v' - (\alpha_2 v^* + \beta_2)] \\ &= \alpha_1 \alpha_2 g(u, v) \end{aligned}$$

and so if $(\bar{u}, \bar{v})$ maximizes $g(u, v)$, it follows that $(\bar{u}', \bar{v}')$ maximizes $g'(u', v')$. Finally, $(\bar{u}, \bar{v})$ satisfies N6. In fact, suppose that S is symmetric in the sense of N6, and $u^* = v^*$. Then $(\bar{v}, \bar{u}) \in S$. But

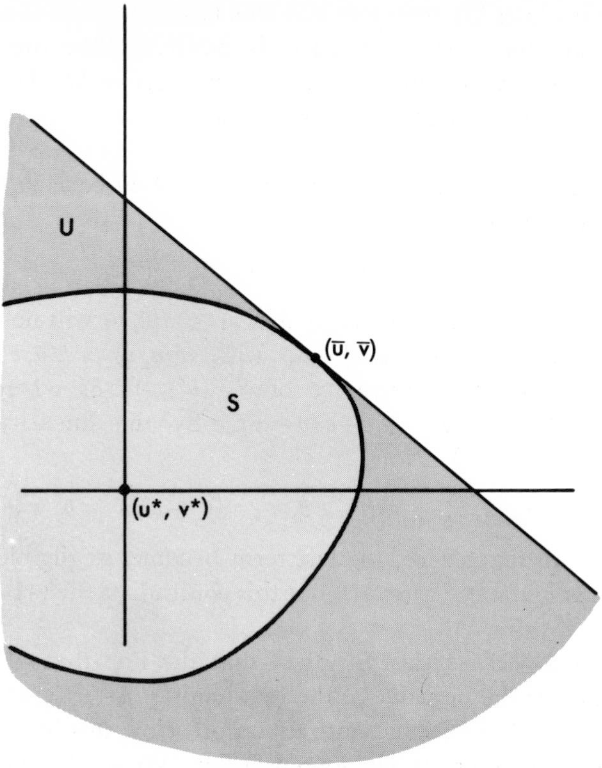

FIGURE VII.2.1

clearly $g(\bar{u}, \bar{v}) = g(\bar{v}, \bar{u})$. Since $(\bar{u}, \bar{v})$ is the unique point which maximizes $g(u, v)$, it follows that $(\bar{u}, \bar{v}) = (\bar{v}, \bar{u})$: i.e., $\bar{u} = \bar{v}$.

We know, thus, that $(\bar{u}, \bar{v})$ satisfies Axioms N1–N6. We must now show that it is the unique rule which satisfies these axioms. Let $(\bar{u},\bar{v})$ be defined, then, as above. Consider the set

$$U = \{(u, v) \mid h(u, v) \leq h(\bar{u}, \bar{v})\}$$

(see Figure VII.2.1). By Lemma VII.2.3, $S \subset U$.

Let T be obtained from U by the linear transformation

$$7.2.3 \qquad \begin{cases} u' = \dfrac{u - u^*}{\bar{u} - u^*} \\[2ex] v' = \dfrac{v - v^*}{\bar{v} - v^*} \cdot \end{cases}$$

It is easy to see that T is simply the set $\{(u', v') \mid u' + v' \leq 2\}$; moreover, $u^{*\prime} = v^{*\prime} = 0$. Because T is symmetric, it follows by

N6 that the solution must lie on the line $u' = v'$; by N3, it must be the point (1, 1). Inverting the transformation VII.2.3, it follows by N5 that $(\bar{u}, \bar{v})$ must be the solution of (U, u^*, v^*). But since $(\bar{u}, \bar{v}) \in S$, it follows that $(\bar{u}, \bar{v})$ must be the solution of (S, u^*, v^*).

Let us suppose, now, that the hypothesis of Lemma VII.2.3 does not hold: i.e., there are no points $(u, v) \in S$ with $u > u^*$, $v > v^*$. By the convexity of S, we know that if there is any $(u, v) \in S$ with $u > u^*$, $v = v^*$, there can be no $(u, v) \in S$ with $v > v^*$. Under these conditions, we simply let $(\bar{u}, \bar{v})$ be the point in S which maximizes u, subject to the constraint $v = v^*$. Similarly, if there is $(u, v) \in S$ with $u = u^*$, $v > v^*$, there can be no $(u, v) \in S$ with $u > u^*$, and we let $(\bar{u}, \bar{v})$ be the point in S which maximizes v, subject to the constraint $u = u^*$. It is easily checked that these solutions satisfy the axioms; it is also easy to see that Axioms N1, N2, and N3 will allow no other solution.

Theorem VII.2.2 shows, then, that Nash's axioms can be satisfied by a unique scheme; we have also shown what Nash's solution is. According to Lemma VII.2.3, if the boundary of S is smooth (i.e., has a tangent) at the point $(\bar{u}, \bar{v})$, the line of constant $h(u, v)$ is tangent to S at that point. Now the slope of the boundary of S, at any point, represents the rate at which utility can be transferred from one player to the other. What Nash's scheme tells us, in brief, is that additional utility must be divided between the two players in a ratio equal to the rate at which this utility can be transferred. Naturally, since utility is not assumed to be linearly transferable, there may be only one point at which utility is transferable at this given rate. Figure VII.2.2 illustrates this.

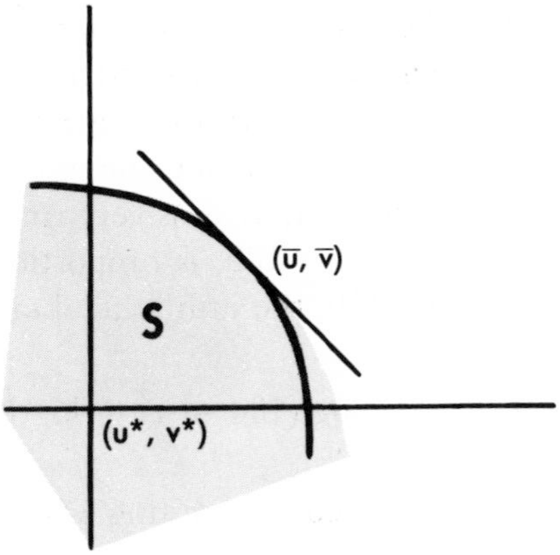

FIGURE VII.2.2

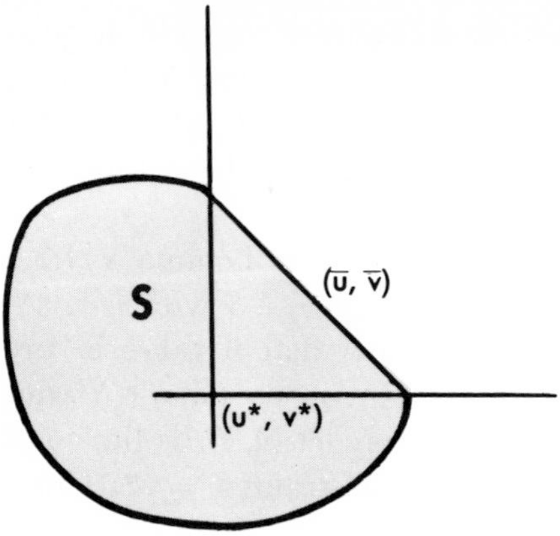

FIGURE VII.2.3

In case the utility is linearly transferable, of course, the problem becomes much simpler. In fact, we may assume (by a change of utility scales if necessary) that the rate at which utility can be transferred is 1:1 (i.e., player I can transfer one unit of utility to II by giving up one unit himself). Thus S contains all the points on or below a certain line $u + v = k$ (where k is the maximum possible utility the two players can obtain together) and above and to the right of (u^*, v^*). (See Figure VII.2.3.) The corresponding Nash solution will be $(\bar{u}, \bar{v})$, where $\bar{u} = (u^* - v^* + k)/2$, and $\bar{v} = (v^* - u^* + k)/2$.

It is easy to see that $\bar{u} + \bar{v} = k$, while $\bar{u} - \bar{v} = u^* - v^*$. Thus in this case, the relative positions of the two players are maintained, while their utilities are increased as much as possible (i.e., the excess utility is divided evenly between the two players).

VII.2.5 Example. Two men are offered \$100 if they can decide how to divide the money. The first man is assumed to be very rich, while the second man has \$100 capital in all. It is assumed that the utility of a sum of money is proportional to its logarithm. How should the money be divided?

As the first player is very rich, we can assume that the utility of \$$x$, with $x \le 100$, is proportional to x. As the second player has only \$100, the utility he obtains from \$$x$ will be

$$\log(100 + x) - \log 100 = \log \frac{100 + x}{100}.$$

(We are, of course, setting $u^* = v^* = 0$.) Thus the set S will consist of the convex hull of (0, 0) and the arc with equation

$$v = \log \frac{200 - u}{100}.$$

As this function is convex, S consists simply of the area bounded by this curve (see Figure VII.2.4); of course, we are only interested in its intersection with the positive quadrant.

Now, we want the point in S which maximizes uv: i.e., the value of u which maximizes

$$g = u \log \frac{200 - u}{100}.$$

When we differentiate and set equal to zero, we obtain the equation

$$\frac{u}{200 - u} = \log \frac{200 - u}{100}.$$

This gives us, approximately, $u \doteq 54.4$: i.e., player I should get approximately \$54.40, while II gets \$45.60.

In a sense, this result seems strange: it implies that the richer person should receive more than the poorer person, who, it might be argued, "needs the money more." In fact, however, this idea implies an interpersonal comparison of utility, which is not generally allowed. The fact is that player II's utility for money decreases rapidly, while I's does not. The result is that II will be very eager to get at least something, and can be "bargained down" by I.

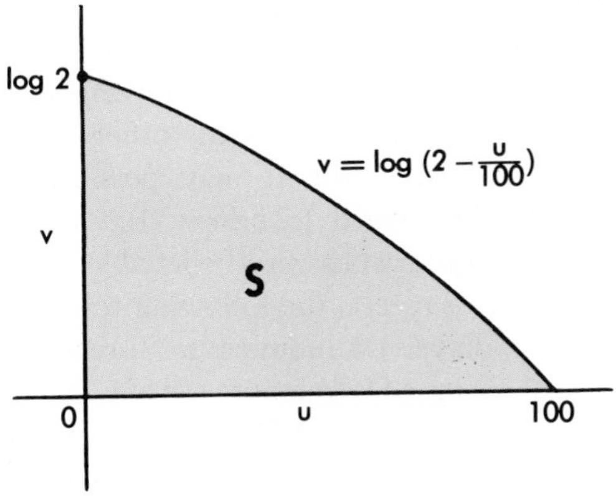

FIGURE VII.2.4

VII.3 THREATS

A serious objection can be raised to Nash's bargaining scheme, and it is that it does not take threats into account. The following example will best outline this objection.

VII.3.1 Example. A worker has the choice of working, in which case he will be paid a subsistence salary while his boss has a profit of \$10, or not working, in which case he will starve, while his boss makes no profit. A reasonable assignment of utilities to these events would be (0, 10) and (−500, 0). The boss, however, may, if he desires, give part of the profit to the worker, so that (assuming utility to be linearly transferable) the set S will include all points below $u + v = 10$, and none other in the positive quadrant. As it is clear that $u^* = v^* = 0$, the Nash solution would seem to be $\bar{u} = \bar{v} = 5$. This disregards, however, the fact that the second player is in a much stronger position than his opponent. In fact, player I cannot prevent II from getting \$10 except by taking a very difficult step; a threat to stop work on his part would not be very believable, and as a result, he will probably continue to work for his subsistence salary.

It is difficult to deny that an example such as this tends to weaken Nash's bargaining solution. Some analysis of threats is in order if we are to correct these weaknesses. Quite generally, a threat is effective if it is believable, and if it tends to improve the position of the threatener vis-à-vis the person being threatened. Thus, a threat to kill someone is generally more effective than a threat to become angry, because the position of the killer is certainly improved vis-à-vis his victim (though in point of fact it may be worsened in absolute terms) while getting angry generally does no such thing. On the other hand, a threat to destroy the whole world, while it may possibly improve the threatener's position in regard to others (reducing them all to equality in nothingness), is not very believable and hence not effective.

Nash suggests the following three-step bargaining scheme:

1. Player I announces a "threat" strategy, x.
2. Player II, in ignorance of x, announces a threat strategy, y.
3. Players I and II bargain. If they can come to an agreement, then that agreement takes effect. If they do not come to an

agreement, then they *must* use their threat strategies, x and y; the payoffs to the two players will be determined in this manner.

The question naturally arises as to the enforcement of these threats; if one of the players makes a wild threat, he may find himself averse to carrying out the threat later on. Some machinery may, however, be devised for this purpose. At any rate, we assume a player is bound to his threat in some manner or other.

In effect, what this means is that the maximin values, u^* and v^*, have been replaced by the threat values, xAy^t and xBy^t. Axioms N1–N5 are now applied, and the result is the solution $(\bar{u}, \bar{v})$ where $(\bar{u}, \bar{v})$ is the point in S which maximizes

$$g(u, v) = (u - xAy^t)(v - xBy^t)$$

(subject, of course, to $u \geq xAy^t$).

A figure will probably explain the workings of this scheme best. In Figure VII.2.5, a typical set S (closed, bounded, and convex) is shown. The curve S^o is the Pareto-optimal boundary of S (i.e., the subset of S which satisfies N3). From each point on S^o at which a tangent to S^o exists, a line is drawn whose slope is the negative of the tangent slope. If the tangent does not exist (as at

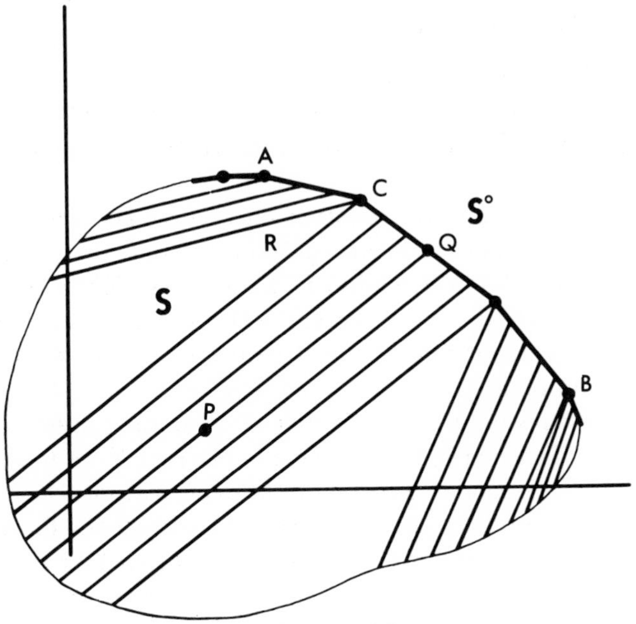

FIGURE VII.2.5

point C) two lines are drawn, corresponding to the right and left tangents to S^o at C. It is easy to see that, by the convexity of S, the lines in this family intersect, if at all, outside of S.

Now, suppose the threat strategies, x and y, give, as threat value, a point such as P, lying on one of these lines. The arbitrated (Nash) value of the game is the point Q at which this line cuts S^o. If, on the other hand, the threat value is at a point such as R (lying inside the angle made by two lines from the same point in S^o) then the arbitrated value will be the point C at which these two lines meet S^o. Thus player I's aim, in choosing his threat strategy, will be to get a point lying on the lowest possible of this family of lines; player II's aim is to get a point on the highest possible of these lines.

To the question that arises as to the existence of equilibrium pairs of threat strategies, the answer can be given that they do exist. (It is, of course, necessary to define equilibrium pairs for such games; this is done in the obvious manner.)

VII.3.1 Theorem. Any bimatrix game has at least one equilibrium pair of threat strategies (x, y).

The objectives of the two players in choosing their threat strategies, however, are directly opposed. Hence it is not difficult to prove the following theorem as well.

VII.3.2 Theorem. If (x', y') and (x'', y'') are equilibrium pairs of threat strategies, then so are (x', y'') and (x'', y'). Moreover, the Nash arbitrated payoff is the same for both (x', y') and (x'', y'').

We shall not give the proofs of Theorems VII.3.1 and VII.3.2 here; they are left as problems, pointing out only that VII.3.1 is a modification of VII.1.2, while VII.3.2 is a very slight modification of Theorem II.1.2. By Theorem VII.3.2, we see that we can actually talk about *optimal* threat strategies (rather than merely equilibrium points).

An interesting problem is that of computing optimal threat strategies. In general, this can be complicated, since the arbitration value corresponding to a pair of threat strategies depends not only on the numbers xAy^t and xBy^t, but also on the form of the Pareto-optimal boundary of the set S. Since all that is required of S is that it be convex, there is no obvious method. In certain cases, however, it might be a simple problem.

If, in particular, utility is linearly transferable between the two players, the problem becomes quite simple. In fact, we can choose the utility scales so that utility is transferable at the rate of 1:1. The obvious adaptation of what we studied above tells us that, if x and y are the threat strategies, the arbitration value will be

$$\bar{u} = \frac{xAy^t - xBy^t + k}{2}$$

$$\bar{v} = \frac{xBy^t - xAy^t + k}{2}$$

where k is the maximum utility that can be obtained by the two working together. But this means player I will be trying to maximize $x(A - B)y^t$, while II will be trying to minimize this same quantity. Thus, the optimal threat strategies for the bimatrix game (A, B) are the same as the optimal strategies for the matrix (zero-sum) game $A - B$, which we know how to solve.

VII.3.3 Example. Consider the bimatrix game (A, B), given by

$$\begin{pmatrix} (1, 4) & (-\frac{4}{3}, -4) \\ (-3, -1) & (4, 1) \end{pmatrix}.$$

Assuming there is no transferable commodity, the set S is the convex hull of the four points (a_{ij}, b_{ij}) shown in Figure VII.2.6. The maximin security levels are seen to be 0 for both players, obtained by the mixed strategies $(\frac{3}{4}, \frac{1}{4})$ and $(\frac{1}{2}, \frac{1}{2})$ respectively. As S is nearly symmetric, it follows that the value, under the first Nash scheme, must be $(\frac{5}{2}, \frac{5}{2})$. On the other hand, this does not take player II's threat possibility into account; in fact, if II uses his first pure strategy, we see that I really can do very little against him.

We should, therefore, consider the threat possibility. We see that, on the Pareto-optimal boundary of S, utility is transferable (by randomization) at the rate 1:1. Thus we can consider the game $A - B$:

$$A - B = \begin{pmatrix} -3 & \frac{8}{3} \\ -2 & 3 \end{pmatrix}.$$

This game has a saddle point at -2. As the maximum total

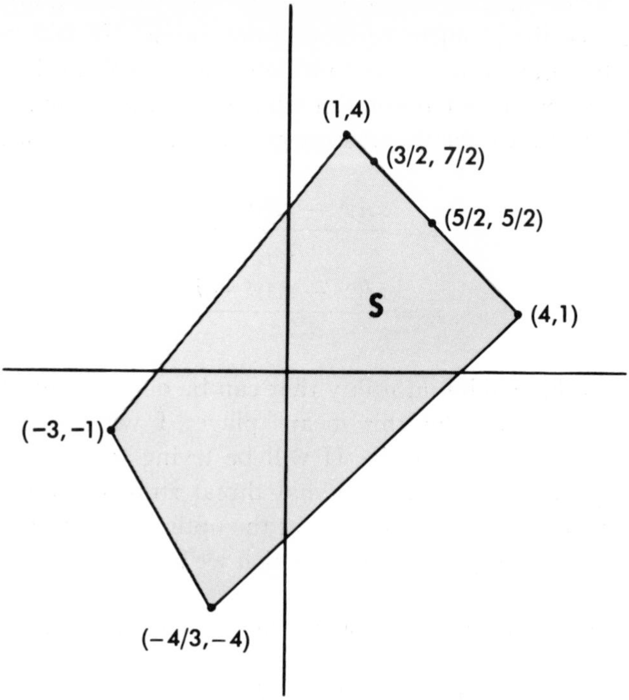

FIGURE VII.2.6

utility for the two players is 5, we obtain the "arbitrated threat solution" $(\frac{3}{2}, \frac{7}{2})$. This certainly takes II's stronger threat possibility into account.

PROBLEMS

1. We think of a bargaining game as a non-cooperative game, in which each player's "strategy" consists of making a demand. Then, if the two demands (u, v) are consistent (belong to S) the players receive their demand; otherwise they receive their minimax (or threat) values, (u^*, v^*).
   (a) Every point on the Pareto-optimal boundary of S is an equilibrium pair.
   (b) Assume $u^* = v^* = 0$, and let g be the characteristic function of S (i.e., $g = 1$ on S and $g = 0$ on the complement of S). Then, if the players demand (u, v), their payoffs will be $(ug(u, v), vg(u, v))$.
   (c) Let h be any non-negative function, and assume that the payoff, in case the demands (u, v) are made, is (uh, vh).

Show that, if $(\bar{u}_h, \bar{v}_h)$ maximizes the function uvh, then $(\bar{u}_h, \bar{v}_h)$ is an equilibrium pair.

(d) Let $h_1, h_2, \ldots$ be a sequence of non-negative continuous functions which converge to g. Then, if $(\bar{u}, \bar{v})$ is the Nash solution (arbitrated value) of the game, there exists a sequence of points $(\bar{u}_j, \bar{v}_j)$, each one of which is an equilibrium point of the demand game with payoff (uh_j, vh_j), which converges to $(\bar{u}, \bar{v})$.

2. Prove the existence of "optimal" threat strategies for the Nash modified bargaining model (Theorems VII.3.1 and VII.3.2).

3. (a) Consider a "supergame" consisting of 100 repetitions of the "prisoner's dilemma." In the supergame, each player has a very large number of pure strategies, each one of which decides what to do at the nth play of the game on the basis of the supergame's "history," (i.e., what has happened on the first $n - 1$ plays). Show that, if two strategies are in equilibrium, use of these two strategies will cause both players to use the "double-cross" (second) strategy at each play of the game.

(b) Show, however, that, for $n > 2$, the supergame strategy σ_n ("Play the first [cooperative] strategy for the first n trials, so long as my opponent does likewise, and double-cross the last $100 - n$ trials") is better in the sense that, against the opponent's optimal response, it gives a better payoff.

(c) Show that if the supergame consists of X trials, where X is a random variable with an exponential distribution $P(n) = ke^{-\alpha n}$, then there exist equilibrium pairs which involve using the cooperative first strategy at each play of the game.

4. It was mentioned, in Problem II.9, that two-person constant-sum games could be solved by the method of "fictitious play." Show that this method cannot be used to obtain equilibrium points of bimatrix games by considering the game (A, B) where

$$A = \begin{pmatrix} 2 & 0 & 1 \\ 1 & 2 & 0 \\ 0 & 1 & 2 \end{pmatrix} \qquad B = \begin{pmatrix} 1 & 0 & 2 \\ 2 & 1 & 0 \\ 0 & 2 & 1 \end{pmatrix}.$$

(a) Assume the players start by choosing (1, 1). There will be a run of (1, 1), followed by a run of (1, 3), then runs of (3, 3), (3, 2), (2, 2), (1, 1), etc., in a cycle.

(b) Each run is at least twice as long as the previous run.

(c) The empirical strategies do not converge at all, but cycle. Neither of the two cycles passes through $(\frac{1}{3}, \frac{1}{3}, \frac{1}{3})$ which is the unique equilibrium point.

CHAPTER VIII

n-PERSON GAMES

VIII.1 NON-COOPERATIVE GAMES

In considering n-person games (where $n \geq 3$), the same distinction will arise as in considering two-person non-zero-sum games. That is, cooperation among some or all of the players may be forbidden or permitted by the rules of the game. Let us consider the first: i.e., the non-cooperative case.

In the non-cooperative case, the principal question is the existence of equilibrium n-tuples. This question is answered by the following theorem:

VIII.1.1 Theorem. Any finite n-person non-cooperative game has at least one equilibrium n-tuple of mixed strategies.

We will not give a proof of VIII.1.1 here. It may be seen, however, that there is no difficulty in extending the proof of Theorem VII.1.2 to this case.

Although Theorem VIII.1.1 is certainly a valuable result, it may be pointed out that all the difficulties which were observed for equilibrium points of bimatrix games are also present here. Moreover, the computation of equilibrium n-tuples (where $n \geq 3$) is incomparably more difficult than the computation of equilibrium pairs.

In general, there is no great difference between the theory of non-cooperative n-person games and non-cooperative two-person general-sum games.

VIII.2 COOPERATIVE GAMES

Let us consider the case in which cooperation is permitted. We have just seen that, in the non-cooperative case, there is very little difference between two-person and n-person games. In fact, the n-person game is merely a generalization of the two-person case. In cooperative games, however, we find that a new idea appears: that of *coalitions*. In the two-person case, there is only one possible coalition. In the n-person case, there are many possible coalitions and this means that, if a coalition is to form and remain for some time, the different members of the coalition must reach some sort of equilibrium or stability. It is this idea of stability that must be analyzed in any meaningful theory.

We can see the meaning of this stability best by taking an example. Consider the following three-person game: Players 1, 2, and 3 are faced with the simple problem of forming a coalition. If any two of them succeed in forming a coalition, then the third player must pay each of them one unit. If no two-player coalition is formed, then there is no payoff at all.

In this simple example, there is really very little to be said. Assuming nothing about the personal relations among the three players, any one of the three possible two-player coalitions might be formed, and there is no way to distinguish among them. Hence the three payoffs $(-2, 1, 1)$, $(1, -2, 1)$, and $(1, 1, -2)$ corresponding to these three coalitions seem to be a "natural" result, and may be considered in some way a "solution" of the game. Alternatively, the payoff $(0, 0, 0)$ which is the average of these three payoffs may also be thought of as some sort of solution to the game. (We shall see later on in what sense these are solutions.)

Let us suppose now that the game is changed slightly, so that, if the coalition $\{2, 3\}$ is formed, player I must pay 1.1 units to 2, and 0.9 unit to 3. This would seem to improve 2's outlook, since he can now gain more from the same action. However, closer analysis will show that this is not so. In fact, the coalition $\{2, 3\}$ now becomes almost impossible to form (unless there is some external difficulty to complicate communications between 1 and

3) since both 1 and 3 stand to gain from forming $\{1, 3\}$. Hence 2 is in a worse position than before; in fact, one of the two possible coalitions he might join is very unstable. He might, however, remedy this by giving 3 a side payment of 0.1 unit (assuming such a side payment is possible). This will reduce the game to the previous game.

The foregoing example should serve to illustrate first, the importance of side payments in this game and second, the need for some sort of stability among the different payoffs in a solution. This latter question will be treated later on; at first we shall deal with side payments.

Once again, the existence of a linearly transferable commodity is in question. Let us assume that this commodity does exist; the theory developed on this assumption will be called the *side-payments theory.*

In the side-payments theory, the utility functions for the several players can be chosen so that the rate of transfer of utility among any two of them is 1:1. As pointed out in the two-person case this means that, if a subset S of the players (coalition) can obtain a total utility v, this utility can be divided among the members of S in any way possible. Thus we will be interested in the total utility which can be attained by any one of these coalitions.

VIII.2.1 Definition. For an n-person game, we shall let $N = \{1, 2, \ldots, n\}$ be the set of all *players.* Any non-empty subset of N (including N itself and all the one-element subsets) is called a *coalition.*

VIII.2.2 Definition. By the *characteristic* function of an n-person game we mean a real-valued function, v, defined on the subsets of N, which assigns to each $S \subset N$ the maximin value (to S) of the two-person game played between S and $N - S$, assuming that these two coalitions form.

Thus $v(S)$ is the amount of utility that the members of S can obtain from the game, whatever the remaining players may do. From this definition, it follows that

8.2.1 $\quad v(\varnothing) = 0$

for obvious reasons. Now if S and T are disjoint coalitions, it is clear that they can accomplish at least as much by joining forces as by remaining separate. Hence we have the *super-additivity* property

8.2.2 $v(S \cup T) \geq v(S) + v(T) \quad \text{if } S \cap T = \varnothing.$

In dealing with two-person games, we have seen that we generally dispense with the extensive form and deal only with the normal form. This is because the normal form allows us to study mixed strategies, which are the essence of such games, with greatest ease. Now, the essence of n-person games is not the randomization; rather, it is the formation of coalitions. Thus we shall study, not the normal form, but the characteristic function. In fact the characteristic function tells us the capacities of the different coalitions, assuming optimal (maximin) randomization, and thus is best suited to study coalitions. In general, we shall identify the game with its characteristic function.

VIII.2.3 Definition. By an *n-person game in characteristic function form* is meant a real-valued function v, defined on the subsets of N, satisfying conditions 8.2.1 and 8.2.2.

Some authors have dispensed with 8.2.2 and studied functions satisfying only the condition $v(\varnothing) = 0$. Very often such functions are called *improper* games, whereas those which also satisfy 8.2.2 are called *proper* games. Unless specifically stated, throughout this book we shall deal only with proper games.

As mentioned above, the amount $v(S)$ is the maximin value of the game played between S and $N - S$. Let us suppose that the normal form of the game is constant sum (i.e., the sum of the utility payoffs to all the players is always the same). The game between S and $N - S$ is then strictly competitive, and it follows, if it is finite, that the minimax theorem holds. Thus we will have

8.2.3 $v(S) + v(N - S) = v(N).$

This leads to the following definition.

VIII.2.4 Definition. A game (in characteristic function form) is said to be constant sum if, for all $S \subset N$,

$$v(S) + v(N - S) = v(N).$$

It should be noted that a game might be constant sum in its characteristic function form without being constant sum in its normal form. (It is even possible for the game to be constant sum in its normal form without being constant sum in its characteristic function form, though this cannot happen with finite games.)

Let us suppose, then, that an n-person game is played. Without inquiring into the particular coalition structure obtained, we might like to know the possible payoff vectors. Now, assuming that some type of understanding is arrived at, the players will have the total utility $v(N)$ to divide. (In a constant-sum game, it is not necessary that an understanding be reached for this to happen.) This can be divided in any way at all, but it is of course clear that no player will accept less than the minimum which he can attain for himself.

VIII.2.5 Definition. An *imputation* (for the n-person game v) is a vector $x = (x_1, \ldots, x_n)$ satisfying

$$\text{(i)} \quad \sum_{i \in N} x_i = v(N)$$

$$\text{(ii)} \quad x_i \geq v(\{i\}) \quad \text{for all } i \in N.$$

We shall use the notation $E(v)$ for the set of all imputations of this game.

It might be argued that, except in the constant-sum case, condition (i) in this definition is too strong, since it is quite likely that the players will fail to reach any understanding, and will wind up obtaining less than the total amount $v(N)$ which they can get. While this is a valid objection, it will be seen later on that many of our "solution concepts" eliminate all vectors which do not satisfy this condition.

The question now is this: which of all the imputations will be obtained? This is, of course, a difficult (or even impossible) problem. There is one condition, however, in which this problem is trivial: that is when the set $E(v)$ has only one element. In this case, that unique imputation will be the obvious result. It does not matter what coalitions form. This gives rise to the distinction between *essential* and *inessential* games. It is clear (by superadditivity, repeated n times) that:

$$8.2.4 \quad v(N) \geq \sum_{i \in N} v(\{i\}).$$

Now, $E(v)$ will have only one point if equality holds in 8.2.4. Thus we have:

VIII.2.6 Definition. A game v is *essential* if

$$v(N) > \sum_{i \in N} v(\{i\}).$$

It is *inessential* otherwise.

It is the essential games which are of interest to us.

VIII.3 DOMINATION. STRATEGIC EQUIVALENCE. NORMALIZATION

Given a game v, let x and y be two imputations. Suppose the players of the game are confronted by a choice between x and y. Can we find any criterion to determine when one of these will be chosen rather than the other?

It is of course clear that, unless $x = y$, there will be some players who prefer x to y (those i such that $x_i > y_i$). Because the two vectors are imputations, however, there will also be some players who prefer y to x. Hence it is not enough merely to state that *some* players prefer x to y. On the other hand, it is not possible that *all* players will prefer x to y (since the sum of the components of either x or y is $v(N)$). What is necessary is that the players who prefer x to y be actually strong enough to enforce the choice of x.

VIII.3.1 Definition. Let x and y be two imputations, and let S be a coalition. We say *x dominates y through S* (notation, $x \succ_S y$) if

$$\text{(i)} \quad x_i > y_i \quad \text{for all } i \in S$$

$$\text{(ii)} \quad \sum_{i \in S} x_i \leq v(S).$$

We say x dominates y (notation, $x \succ y$) if there is any coalition S such that $x \succ_S y$.

Thus condition (i) states that the members of S all prefer x to y; condition (ii) states that they are capable of obtaining what x gives them.

It is easy to see that the relation $\succ_S$ (for any given S) is a partial order relation. On the other hand, the relation $\succ$, while it is irreflexive, is neither transitive nor anti-symmetric (since the coalition S may be different in different cases). This is a serious difficulty; it will certainly complicate things for us later on.

Since we plan to analyze games by means of the domination relation, we are naturally interested in games whose imputation sets have the same domination structure.

VIII.3.2 Definition. Two n-person games, u and v, are said to be *isomorphic* if there exists a 1–1 function, f, mapping $E(u)$ onto $E(v)$ in such a way that, for $x, y \in E(u)$, and $S \subset N$, $x \succ_S y \leftrightarrow f(x) \succ_S f(y)$.

It may be difficult to tell whether two games are isomorphic in this sense. We have, however, the following criterion:

VIII.3.3 Definition. Two n-person games, u and v, are said to be *S-equivalent* if there exist a positive number, r, and n real constants $\alpha_1, \ldots, \alpha_n$, such that, for all $S \subset N$,

$$v(S) = ru(S) + \sum_{i \in S} \alpha_i.$$

Essentially, if two games are S-equivalent, we can obtain one from the other simply by performing a linear transformation on the utility spaces of the several players. It is easy to prove that S-equivalence implies isomorphism:

VIII.3.4 Theorem. If u and v are S-equivalent, they are isomorphic.

PROOF: Assume u and v are S-equivalent. Consider the function, defined on $E(u)$,

$$f(x) = rx + \alpha$$

where r and $\alpha = (\alpha_1, \ldots, \alpha_j)$ are as in VIII.3.3. It is easy to check that, if $x \in E(u)$, $f(x) \in E(v)$. Moreover, if $x \succ_S y$, it is clear that $f(x) \succ_S f(y)$. Hence f is the desired isomorphism.

Thus S-equivalence is sufficient for isomorphism. (The converse of this theorem, while true, is rather lengthy to prove and so we shall make no attempt to do so. See Reference VIII.5.)

It is obvious that S-equivalence is, indeed, an equivalence relation. It is interesting to choose one particular game from each equivalence class.

VIII.3.5 Definition. A game, v, is said to be in *(0, 1) normalization* if

$$\text{(i)} \quad v(\{i\}) = 0 \quad \text{for all } i \in N$$

$$\text{(ii)} \quad v(N) = 1.$$

VIII.3.6 Theorem. If u is an essential game, it is S-equivalent to exactly one game in (0, 1) normalization.

Theorem VIII.3.6, whose proof we omit (it is trivial), tells us that we can choose a game in (0, 1) normalization to represent each equivalence class of games. The advantage of choosing such a game is that, in such a game, the value $v(S)$ of a coalition tells us directly its strength (i.e., the extra amounts which its members gain in forming it), and that all its imputations are probability vectors.

Other types of normalization have been used in the literature of n-person games. A common normalization is $(-1, 0)$ normalization, in which $v(\{i\}) = -1$ and $v(N) = 0$. We shall, however, deal with games in (0, 1) normalization throughout. As our interest is in essential games, this entails no loss of generality.

The set of n-person games in (0, 1) normalization is the set of all real-valued functions, v, defined on the subsets of N, such that

8.3.1 $v(\varnothing) = 0$

8.3.2 $v(\{i\}) = 0$ for all $i \in N$

8.3.3 $v(N) = 1$

8.3.4 $v(S \cup T) \geq v(S) + v(T)$ if $S \cap T = \varnothing$.

These four conditions determine a $(2^n - n - 2)$-dimensional convex set. If the game is constant sum, we have the additional condition

8.3.5 $v(N - S) = v(N) - v(S)$ for all $S \subset N$.

This gives $2^{n-1} - 1$ new equations, so that the set of constant-sum games has dimension $2^{n-1} - n - 1$. Thus it is clear that the dimension of the set of n-person constant-sum games is the same as that of the set of $(n - 1)$-person games. In fact, the two sets are congruent.

Indeed, if u is an $(n - 1)$-person game in (0, 1) normalization, it may be expanded to an n-person constant-sum game, v, by the addition of a new player, n, setting:

$$v(S) = u(S) \quad \text{if } n \notin S$$
$$v(S) = 1 - u(N - S) \quad \text{if } n \in S.$$

It is easily checked that this game is constant sum.

There are two special types of games which are of interest:

VIII.3.7 Definition. A game, v, is said to be *symmetric* if $v(S)$ depends only on the number of elements in S.

VIII.3.8 Definition. A game, v, in (0, 1) normalization is said to be *simple* if, for each $S \subset N$, we have either $v(S) = 0$ or $v(S) = 1$. A game is simple if its (0, 1) normalization is simple.

Essentially, a simple set is one in which every coalition is either winning (value 1) or losing (value 0), with nothing in between. As such, simple games are applicable to political science, as they include voting "games" in elections and legislatures.

VIII.4 THE CORE. STABLE SETS

Let us proceed, then, to the analysis of games in terms of the domination relation. An obvious first idea is to study the undominated imputations.

VIII.4.1 Definition. The set of all undominated imputations for a game, v, is called the *core*. The notation for the core is $C(v)$.

VIII.4.2 Theorem. The core of a game, v, is the set of all n-vectors, x, satisfying

$$\text{(a)} \quad \sum_{i \in S} x_i \geq v(S) \quad \text{for all } S \subset N$$

$$\text{(b)} \quad \sum_{i \in S} x_i = v(N).$$

PROOF: If we let $S = \{i\}$, condition (a) reduces to $x_i \geq v(\{i\})$. This, together with condition (b), means that all such vectors are imputations.

Let us suppose that x satisfies (a) and (b), and that $y_i > x_i$

for all $i \in S$. But this, together with (a), means that

$$\sum_{i \in S} y_i > v(S)$$

and so it is not possible that $y \succ_S x$. Hence $x \in C(v)$.

Conversely, suppose that y does not satisfy (a) and (b). If it fails to satisfy (b), it is not even an imputation and hence not in $C(v)$. Suppose, then, that there is some non-empty $S \subset N$ such that

$$\sum_{i \in S} y_i = v(S) - \varepsilon$$

where $\varepsilon > 0$. Let

$$\alpha = v(N) - v(S) - \sum_{i \in N-S} v(\{i\}).$$

It is easy to see, by super-additivity, that $\alpha \geq 0$. Finally, let s be the number of elements in S. Now, define z by

$$z_i = \begin{cases} y_i + \dfrac{\varepsilon}{s} & \text{if } i \in S \\[2ex] v(\{i\}) + \dfrac{\alpha}{n - s} & \text{if } i \notin S. \end{cases}$$

It is easily seen that z is an imputation and, moreover, $z \succ_S y$. Hence $y \notin C(v)$.

Theorem VIII.4.2 shows that $C(v)$ is a closed convex set (as it is characterized by a set of loose linear inequalities). This is most interesting, since classical economic theory usually gives the core as "solution" to most game-theoretic problems. Any imputation in the core is stable, in that there is no coalition with both the desire and the power to change the outcome of the game.

Generally, of course, the core may have more than one point. This is not a great handicap; it simply means that more than one outcome is stable. A greater difficulty with the core, however, is that it need not exist (i.e., it may be empty).

VIII.4.3 Theorem. If v is an *essential* constant-sum game, $C(v) = \varnothing$.

PROOF: Suppose $x \in C(v)$. For any $i \in N$, we know

$$\sum_{j \in N-\{i\}} x_j \geq v(N - \{i\})$$

but, by the constant-sum property,

$$v(N - \{i\}) = v(N) - v(\{i\})$$

and, since x is an imputation, we must have $x_i \leq v(\{i\})$. Because v is essential, then

$$\sum x_i \leq \sum v(\{i\}) < v(N)$$

but this means $x \notin E(v)$. The contradiction proves $C(v)$ is empty.

Inasmuch as the core is often empty, it becomes necessary to look for some other type of solution concept. Such a concept is that of *stable sets*. We give first a heuristic justification for the concept.

In VIII.2 we gave an example of a three-person game whose characteristic function can be given most easily in the form

$$v(S) = \begin{cases} -2 & \text{if } S \text{ has 1 member} \\ 2 & \text{if } S \text{ has 2 members} \\ 0 & \text{if } S \text{ has 3 members.} \end{cases}$$

We can leave the game in this form, or put it into (0, 1) normalization. (This can be done by setting $r = \frac{1}{6}$, $\alpha_1 = \alpha_2 = \alpha_3 = \frac{1}{3}$.) The (0, 1) normalization is a simple game in which two- and three-person coalitions win and single-player coalitions lose.

For this game in (0, 1) normalization, we obtain the three imputations

$$\alpha_{12} = (\tfrac{1}{2}, \tfrac{1}{2}, 0)$$
$$\alpha_{13} = (\tfrac{1}{2}, 0, \tfrac{1}{2})$$
$$\alpha_{23} = (0, \tfrac{1}{2}, \tfrac{1}{2})$$

as a "solution." Now, in which sense is this a solution? It is easy to see that none of these three imputations dominates any one of the others. (It was this domination, in fact, which caused us to disallow the three slightly altered imputations in the subsequent variant of the game.) Of course, this is not all; any set consisting of a single imputation would have this property. This set of imputations has also, however, the following property: *any imputation other than the 3 α_{ij} is dominated by one of these three imputations.*

To see this, let $x = (x_1, x_2, x_3)$ be any imputation for this game. As the game is in (0, 1) normalization, we know $x_i \geq 0$ and $x_1 + x_2 + x_3 = 1$. Thus, at most two of the components of x can be as large as $\frac{1}{2}$. If this actually happens, then both of those components must equal $\frac{1}{2}$, while the remaining component is zero.

But this means x is one of the α_{ij}. If, then, x is any other imputation, then at most one of the components can be as large as $\frac{1}{2}$. At least two components, say x_i and x_j, with $i < j$, are then smaller than $\frac{1}{2}$. But it is then clear that $\alpha_{ij} \succ x$ through the set $\{i, j\}$.

This gives us, then, a definition for our "solution concept":

VIII.4.4 Definition. A set $V \subset E(v)$ is said to be a *stable set* for v if:

(i) If $x, y \in V$, then $x \not\succ y$

(ii) If $x \notin V$, then there is some $y \in V$ such that $y \succ x$.

Thus, a stable set satisfies the two conditions of *internal stability* (no imputation in V dominates another) and *external stability* (any imputation outside V is dominated by some imputation in V).

Stable sets were first defined by von Neumann and Morgenstern; they are often called *solutions* of the game. We do not use this name, inasmuch as many other solution concepts have been formulated since then.

One of the principal difficulties with stable sets is that, from their definition, neither existence nor uniqueness is guaranteed. In fact, no general proof of the existence of stable sets has yet been given. On the other hand, no n-person game has been given which does not possess a stable set; indeed, most of them possess immense collections of stable sets (though there are a few with a unique stable set).*

VIII.4.5 Example. Let us consider once again the constant-sum three-person game in (0, 1) normalization. As mentioned above, the set

$$V = \{(\tfrac{1}{2}, \tfrac{1}{2}, 0), (\tfrac{1}{2}, 0, \tfrac{1}{2}), (0, \tfrac{1}{2}, \tfrac{1}{2})\}$$

is stable. However, it is not the only stable set; if c is any number in the interval $[0, \frac{1}{2})$, it is easy to check that the set

$$V_{3,c} = \{(x_1, 1 - c - x_1, c) \mid 0 \le x_1 \le 1 - c\}$$

in which the third player receives the constant c, while players 1 and 2 split the remainder in all possible ways, is also stable. Internal stability follows from the fact that two such imputations,

* A 10-person game which has no stable set solutions has recently been constructed. See Lucas, W. F. *A Game with no Solution*. RAND Memorandum RM-5518-PR, The RAND Corporation, October 1967.

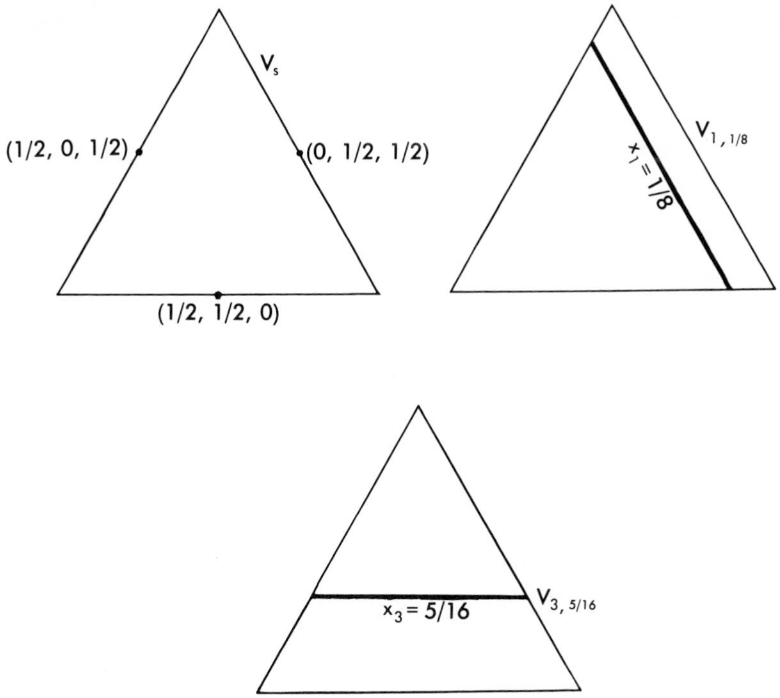

FIGURE VIII.4.1. Three stable set solutions to the three-person constant-sum game.

x and y, differ only in that, say, $x_1 > y_1$, while $x_2 < y_2$. But domination of imputations is not possible through single-player coalitions.

To show that $V_{3,c}$ is externally stable, suppose y is any imputation not in $V_{3,c}$. This means either $y_3 > c$ or $y_3 < c$.

If $y_3 > c$, say $y_3 = c + \varepsilon$. We define x by:

$$x_1 = y_1 + \varepsilon/2$$
$$x_2 = y_2 + \varepsilon/2$$
$$x_3 = c.$$

It is then easy to see that $x \in V_{3,c}$ and $x \succ y$ through $\{1, 2\}$.

If $y_3 < c$, we know that either $y_1 \leq \frac{1}{2}$ or $y_2 \leq \frac{1}{2}$ (or else their sum would be greater than 1). Say $y_1 \leq \frac{1}{2}$. Then let $x = (1 - c, 0, c)$. It is clear that $1 - c > \frac{1}{2} \geq y$, and so $x \succ y$ through $\{1, 3\}$. Clearly, $x \in V_{3,c}$. If $y_2 \leq \frac{1}{2}$, we see similarly that $z \succ y$, where $z = (0, 1 - c, c)$.

Thus it is clear that, apart from the symmetric stable set,

this game has a family of solutions in which player 3 receives a fixed amount c in the interval $[0, \frac{1}{2})$. These are called *discriminatory* stable sets; player 3 is said to be discriminated. In the set $V_{3,0}$, player 3 is said to be totally discriminated, or *excluded*.

By the symmetry of the game, it is clear that there will also exist two families of stable sets, $V_{1,c}$ and $V_{2,c}$, in which players 1 and 2, respectively, are discriminated.

The preceding example shows that a game may possess a bewildering multiplicity of stable sets. It is not clear how one stable set is to be chosen from among all these sets. Nor is it clear, once a stable set is chosen, how an imputation can be chosen from this stable set. Von Neumann and Morgenstern suggest that stable sets are standards of behavior, proper to a given social order. Once a society has decided on the standard of behavior (stable set), the individual players' bargaining abilities would determine the imputation.

As mentioned above, no proof has yet been given of the existence of stable sets for games in general. Partial results have been obtained, however. Some of these results prove the existence of stable sets for certain types of games, and others study the existence of certain types of stable sets.

Let us consider the following theorems:

VIII.4.6 Theorem. Let v be a simple game in (0, 1) normalization, and let S be a *minimal* winning coalition (i.e., a coalition such that $v(S) = 1$ but $v(T) = 0$ for all $T \subset S$, $T \neq S$). Let V_S be the set of all imputations x such that $x_i = 0$ for all $i \notin S$. Then V_S is a stable set.

PROOF: The proof of this theorem is the same as the proof (in Example VIII.4.5) that the set $V_{3,c}$ is stable.

Theorem VIII.4.6 states that every simple game has discriminatory stable sets in which a minimal winning coalition excludes all the others. In certain cases, it is possible that some of the discriminated players will receive small amounts (see Example VIII.4.5). The exact values which they may receive are often quite difficult to determine; we shall not attempt to deal with this question here.

VIII.4.7 Example (Symmetric Solutions to Three-person Games).

In Example VIII.4.6 we gave all stable set solutions to the constant-sum three-person game. We shall see how the symmetric, three-point stable set generalizes to a symmetric stable set for other (general-sum) symmetric three-person games.

For a three-person game in (0, 1) normalization, the values of the one- and three-person coalitions are known in advance, hence it is only the values of the two-person coalitions that remain to be fixed. For symmetric games, these all have the same value, and thus there is a unique parameter, v_2, which determines these games. This parameter can vary throughout the interval [0, 1]; for $v_2 = 1$, we have the constant-sum game (which we have already analyzed), while for $v_2 = 0$ we have a "pure bargaining game" in which every imputation belongs to the core, so that the core is the unique stable set.

When v_2 is large (i.e., close to 1), the players may be expected to behave very much as in the constant-sum game. Thus, they will first attempt to enter into a two-player coalition. Since they are bidding against each other, they cannot ask too much of their presumptive partner, and the "natural" result may be an agreement, between the members of whichever coalition forms, to divide their winnings equally.

Once a two-player coalition has been formed, its members will bargain with the remaining player to determine the division of the remaining $1 - v_2$ units of utility. In this case there are no alternatives; there is no one else to bargain with, and so the amount which the coalition receives depends only on the bargaining abilities of the three players. Thus we may expect to find a stable set consisting of the three line-segments

8.4.1 $$\begin{Bmatrix}(x, x, 1 - 2x)\\(x, 1 - 2x, x)\\(1 - 2x, x, x)\end{Bmatrix} \qquad v_2/2 \le x \le \tfrac{1}{2}.$$

(See Figure VIII.4.2.) It is necessary to check whether this set is, indeed, stable. If we do so, we find that the set is stable for $v_2 \ge \frac{2}{3}$.

Internal stability is proved as follows: since $x \ge v_2/2$, we know that $2x \ge v_2$, and so an imputation of the form $(x, x, 1 - 2x)$ can only be dominated through one of the two coalitions {1, 3} and {2, 3}. But none of the imputations given by 8.4.1 can

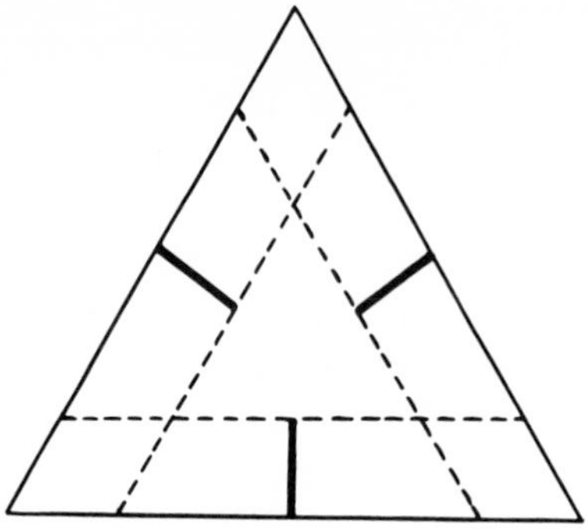

FIGURE VIII.4.2

dominate $(x, x, 1 - 2x)$ through $\{1, 3\}$. For, in an imputation $(y, y, 1 - 2y)$, if $y > x$, then $1 - 2x > 1 - 2y$, while in an imputation $(y, 1 - 2y, y)$, we find that, if $y > x$, then $2y > v_2$ and so the set $\{1, 3\}$ is not effective. Symmetry and similar considerations complete the proof of internal stability.

External stability is also easily proved. Since $v_2 \geq \frac{2}{3}$, we know that any imputation will have at most two components greater than or equal to $v_2/2$, with the single exception of the case $v_2 = \frac{2}{3}$ and the imputation $(\frac{1}{3}, \frac{1}{3}, \frac{1}{3})$, which will in this case satisfy 8.4.1. Thus any imputation which does not satisfy 8.4.1 will have at most two components greater than or equal to $v_2/2$. Let us suppose an imputation z has two such components; by symmetry we may assume these are the first two components, z_1 and z_2. If $z_1 = z_2$, then z satisfies 8.4.1. If $z_1 \neq z_2$, we may (again by symmetry) assume $z_1 = z_2 + 3\varepsilon$, with $\varepsilon > 0$. Then z is dominated by the imputation

$$(z_2 + \varepsilon,\ z_2 + \varepsilon,\ z_3 + \varepsilon)$$

through the coalition $\{2, 3\}$.

If, however, the imputation z has one component or none as great as $v_2/2$, then we may assume that both z_1 and z_2 are smaller than $v_2/2$. Then z is dominated by

$$(v_2/2,\ v_2/2,\ 1 - v_2)$$

through the coalition $\{1, 2\}$.

The above analysis loses its validity for $v_2 < \frac{2}{3}$. In fact, internal stability will be preserved, but the external stability is lost. Such games will possess a core, consisting of all imputations $y = (y_1, y_2, y_3)$ satisfying $y_i \leq 1 - v_2$ for all $i = 1, 2, 3$. It may

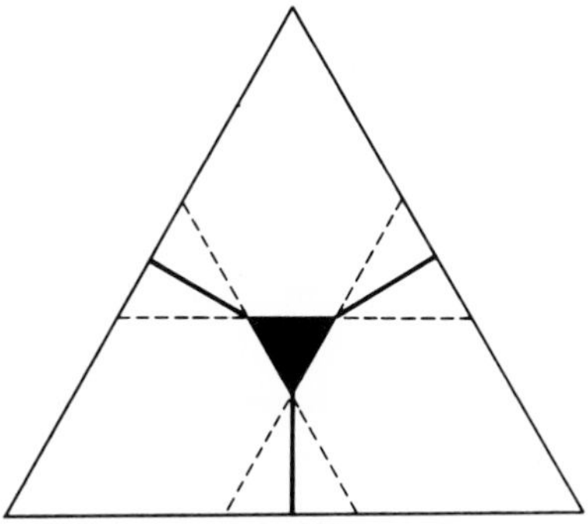

FIGURE VIII.4.3

then be checked that the union of the core and the three line-segments given in 8.4.1 is a stable set (see Figure VIII.4.3). For $v_2 \leq \frac{1}{2}$, moreover, the three line-segments will all be subsets of the core; in this case, thus, the core is the unique stable set (see Figure VIII.4.4).

As we have seen, the set of all n-person games (in normalization) forms a compact subset of $(2^n - n - 2)$-dimensional Euclidean space. Applying Lebesgue measure, we can say that any full-dimensional subset of this set is a *positive fraction* of the set of n-person games. We give these theorems without proof:

VIII.4.8 Theorem. A positive fraction of all n-person games have unique stable sets consisting of the core.

VIII.4.9 Theorem. A positive fraction of all n-person games have stable sets which discriminate $n - 2$ players. In such sets, at least $n - 3$ of the discriminated players are excluded.

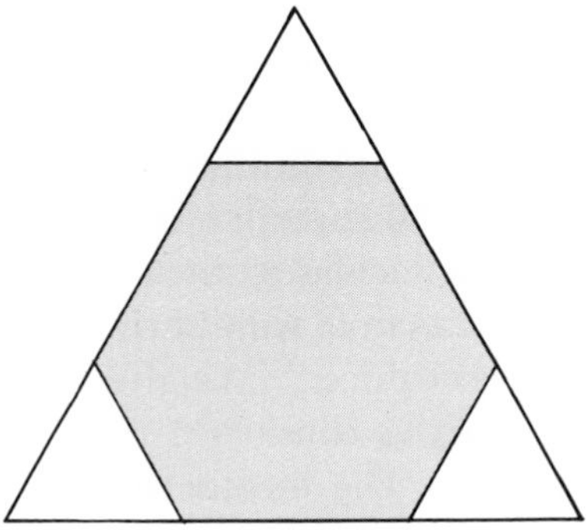

FIGURE VIII.4.4

VIII.5 EDGEWORTH MARKET GAMES—AN EXAMPLE

We have concerned ourselves throughout this chapter with some strictly mathematical ideas. We will now apply some of these to economic analysis.

Let us consider the following type of two-person non-zero sum game: Player I has a units of one commodity while player II has b units of a second commodity. Neither has any units of the other player's commodity. We represent this by saying that player I has the bundle $(a, 0)$ while II has the bundle $(0, b)$. Now, the two are to trade with each other, the idea being that both can gain some utility by changing to the bundles (x, y) and $(a - x, b - y)$, where $0 \leq x \leq a$ and $0 \leq y \leq b$.

Games such as this were first considered by Edgeworth. He gave a "solution" quite analogous to the von Neumann–Morgenstern stable sets. In fact, it is a set of distributions A such that no distribution in A is preferred by both players to any other distribution in A but, if $((x, y); (a - x, b - y))$ is any distribution not in A, there will be some distribution $((x', y'); (a - x', b - y'))$ in A which is preferred by both players. Finally, for any distribution in A, both players have at least as much utility as for the "initial" distribution $((a, 0), (0, b))$. Assuming infinite divisibility of the commodities traded, this set A will usually form a curve, and is called the *contract curve.*

The contract curve is shown graphically in Figure VIII.5.1 by a system of *indifference curves.* These are such that any two points on one of the curves which are convex downward represent the same utility for player I, while any two points on one of the curves which are convex upward represent the same utility for player II. The contract curve will then be the locus of points of tangency of the curves from the two families, restricted to keep both players' utilities at or above the "point of no trading."

In Edgeworth's analysis he concludes that, if the number of players increases, then under certain plausible conditions the contract curve will "shrink" to a single limiting point. This is the "market price." We give below a mathematical interpretation.

Let us consider a market consisting of a set $I = M \cup N$ of traders. The members i of M have initial commodity bundles $(a_i, 0)$, while the members j of N have initial bundles $(0, b_j)$. Each

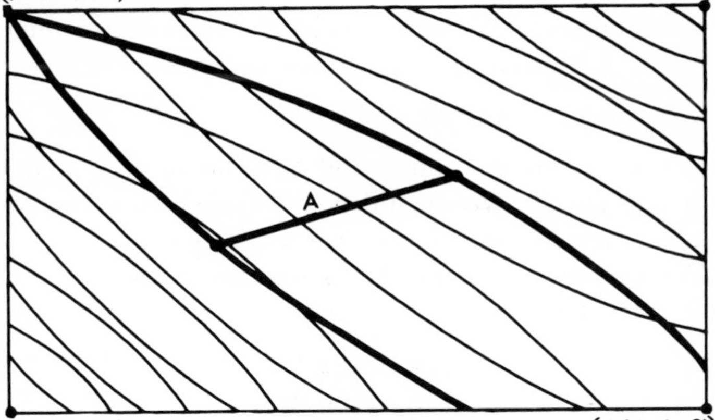

FIGURE VIII.5.1

player, i, has a utility function $\psi_i(x, y)$. We assume

8.5.1 Each ψ_i is strictly convex

8.5.2 $\lim_{x \to \infty} \psi_i(x, y) < \infty$ for each x

8.5.3 $\lim_{y \to \infty} \psi_i(x, y) < \infty$ for each y

8.5.4 The second partial derivatives of each ψ_i exist and are continuous everywhere.

Assume that the coalition S forms. The members of S will divide their joint bundle in such a way as to maximize their total utility, and then possibly make some side payments. We have, thus,

8.5.5 $$v(S) = \max_{x,y} \left\{ \sum_{k \in S} \psi_k(x_k, y_k) \right\}$$

where the maximum is taken over all x, y such that $x_k \geq 0, y_k \geq 0$, $\sum_{k \in S} x_k = \sum_{i \in S \cap M} a_i$, and $\sum_{k \in S} y_k = \sum_{j \in S \cap N} b_j$.

We shall simplify matters by assuming that all players have the same utility function, i.e.,

$$\psi_i(x, y) = \psi(x, y) \quad \text{for all } i.$$

Then, by the strict convexity of ψ, the optimal distribution of goods is obtained by distributing these equally. We assume also that each member of M has the same amount, a, of the first commodity, while each member of N has an amount, b, of the second commodity. We can now give the characteristic function implicitly; it is given by

8.5.6 $v(S) = s\psi(s_m a/s,\ s_n b/s)$

where s, s_m, s_n are the number of elements in S, $S \cap M$, and $S \cap N$ respectively. We shall denote a game such as this, where M has m elements and N has n elements, by $[m, n]$.

We can now look at the two-person game $[1, 1]$. The characteristic function is

$$\begin{aligned} v(\{1\}) &= \psi(a, 0) \\ v(\{2\}) &= \psi(0, b) \\ v(\{1, 2\}) &= 2\psi(a/2, b/2). \end{aligned}$$

This game will have a unique stable set solution consisting of all its imputations: i.e., of all vectors of the form (z_1, z_2), where

8.5.7 $z_1 + z_2 = 2\psi(a/2, b/2)$

8.5.8 $z_1 \geq \psi(a, 0)$

8.5.9 $z_2 \geq \psi(0, b)$.

We will show now that for any n the game $[n, n]$ has a stable set solution analogous to that given by (8.5.7)–(8.5.9).

VIII.5.2 Theorem. For any n, the game $[n, n]$ has a stable set solution, V, consisting of all vectors x with $x_i = z_1$ for $i \in M$ and $x_j = z_2$ for $j \in N$, where (z_1, z_2) satisfies (8.5.7)–(8.5.9).

PROOF: First, V is internally stable. In fact, domination must be through a set S such that $S \cap M \neq \varnothing$ and $S \cap N \neq \varnothing$. But, for $x, y \in V$, if $x_i > y_i$ for some $i \in M$, then $x_j < y_j$ for all $j \in N$. Hence we cannot have $x \succ y$.

Next suppose $x \notin V$. There is some pair (i, j), with $i \in M$, $j \in N$, such that $x_i + x_j < 2\psi(a/2, b/2)$. Choose $(\hat{z}_1, \hat{z}_2)$ then, so that $\hat{z}_1 > x_i$ and $\hat{z}_2 > x_j$. Then the imputation $y \in V$ corresponding to $(\hat{z}_1, \hat{z}_2)$ clearly dominates x through $\{i, j\}$. Thus V is externally stable.

Of course this shows that the stable set solutions have no tendency to "shrink" as n is increased. Such a tendency, however, is shown by the *core*. We consider two cases: monopoly (the game

$[1, n]$) and pure competition (the game $[m, n]$ where both m and n are large).

VIII.5.3 Theorem. In the game $[1, n]$, the imputation x, such that $x_j = \psi(0, b)$ for all $j \in N$, belongs to the core. Moreover, given any $\varepsilon > 0$, there exists an $n(\varepsilon)$ such that, if $n \geq n(\varepsilon)$, no imputation y with $y_1 \leq x_1 - \varepsilon$ can belong to the core.

PROOF: Domination is possible only through a set S with $1 \in S$. As x_1 is as large as possible, it follows that $x \in C(v)$.

Consider now the expression $v(I) - v(I - \{j\}) - \psi(0, b)$, where $j \in N$. If we replace v by its definition 8.5.6, and apply Taylor's theorem, we see that, for any $\varepsilon > 0$, if $n(\varepsilon)$ is large enough,

$$|v(I) - v(I - \{j\}) - \psi(0, b)| < \varepsilon/n$$

for all $n \geq n(\varepsilon)$. Suppose now that y is an imputation for the game $[1, n]$ such that $y_1 \leq x_1 - \varepsilon$. We must have some $j \in N$ such that $y_j \geq \psi(0, b) + \varepsilon/n$ (since we must have $\sum y_i = x_1 + n\psi(0, b)$). Now, it is clear that

$$\sum_{i \in I - \{j\}} y_i \leq v(I) - \psi(0, b) - \varepsilon/n < v(I - \{j\})$$

and so $y \notin C(v)$.

Theorem VIII.5.3 describes what happens in the case of monopoly. For the case of pure competition, we have:

VIII.5.4 Theorem. Suppose m' and n' are such that

$$\psi\left(\frac{m'a}{m' + n'}, \frac{n'b}{m' + n'}\right) = \max_s \psi\left(\frac{s_m a}{s}, \frac{s_n b}{s}\right) \tag{8.5.10}$$

Then, for the game $[m, n]$ where $m = km'$ and $n = kn'$, the imputation

$$x = \left(\frac{v(I)}{m + n}, \frac{v(I)}{m + n}, \ldots, \frac{v(I)}{m + n}\right)$$

is always in the core. Moreover, for any $\varepsilon > 0$, there exists a $k(\varepsilon)$ such that, for any game $[km', kn']$ with $k \geq k(\varepsilon)$, no imputation with a component smaller than $\dfrac{v(I)}{m + n} - \varepsilon$ can belong to the core.

We skip the proof of this theorem, which is quite similar to that of VIII.5.3. Equation 8.5.10 says that the sizes of the two sets of players, M and N, are in "optimal ratio" (e.g., the case when the amount of available capital is just enough to employ all the available labor). If M and N are in any other ratio, there will be some maladjustment (unemployment or overemployment) and there will be no core if the game is sufficiently large. On the other hand, if 8.5.10 holds, there will always be a core which shrinks to the single imputation, x, and our game can increase merrily in size with everybody happy.

PROBLEMS

1. (a) The core of any n-person game, v, is always a subset of any stable set.
   (b) If the core has a non-empty intersection with each face $x_i = v(\{i\})$ of the simplex of imputations, then the core is the unique stable set solution of the game v, and conversely.
   (c) A positive (full-dimensional) fraction of n-person games (in (0, 1) normalization) has a unique stable set solution (Theorem VIII.4.7).

2. For a game v, define a semi-imputation as a vector $x = (x_1, \ldots, x_n)$ such that $x_i \geq v(\{i\})$ and $\sum_{i \in N} x_i \leq v(N)$. Then, if V is any stable set solution to v and x is a semi-imputation but $x \notin V$, there exists $y \in V$ such that $y \succ x$.

3. For a game v, define the number b_i as

$$b_i = \max_{S \subset N - \{i\}} [v(S \cup \{i\}) - v(S)].$$

Show that an imputation x which does not satisfy $x_i \leq b_i$ cannot belong to the core or to any stable set.

4. Show that the symmetric stable set solution V of the three-person game considered in VIII.4.5 generalizes, as follows, to the *main simple solution* of a simple game.

   Let v be a simple, constant-sum n-person game in (0, 1) normalization, and suppose there exists a vector $\alpha = (\alpha_1, \ldots, \alpha_n)$ such that $\alpha_i \geq 0$ and $\sum_{i \in S} \alpha_i = 1$ for every minimal winning coalition S. For such a coalition, let x^S be the vector defined by $x_i^S = \alpha_i$ if $i \in S$, $x_i^S = 0$ otherwise. Then x^S is an imputation, and the set $V = \{x^S \mid S \text{ is a minimal winning coalition}\}$ is a stable set solution of v, called a *main simple solution.*

5. Consider the simple n-person game in (0, 1) normalization in which the winning coalitions consist of (a) player 1 and at least one other player, (b) the set $\{2, 3, \ldots, n\}$.
   (a) Find the main simple solution of this game.
   (b) For $S = \{1, j\}$, where $j \neq 1$, let V_S consist of all the imputations such that $x_1 + x_j = 1$. For $S = \{2, 3, \ldots, n\}$, let V_S consist of all the imputations such that $x_1 = 0$. In either case, V_S is a stable set solution.
   (c) For $S = \{2, 3, \ldots, n\}$ and $0 \leq c \leq 1$, let $V_S(c)$ consist of all the imputations such that $x_1 = c$. Then $V_S(c)$ is a stable set for $0 \leq c < \dfrac{n-2}{n-1}$, but not for $c \geq \dfrac{n-2}{n-1}$.
   (d) For $S = \{1, j\}$ the only stable set solution which discriminates the members of $N - S$ is the set V_S mentioned in (b) above.

6. *Composition of Simple Games.*

Let $v_1, v_2, \ldots, v_n$ be simple games in (0, 1) normalization for $m_1, m_2, \ldots, m_n$ players respectively and let w be an n-person game in (0, 1) normalization. Let $V_1, V_2, \ldots, V_n, W$ be stable set solutions to $v_1, v_2, \ldots, v_n, w$ respectively.

Form a simple m-person game, u (where $m = m_1 + m_2 + \cdots + m_n$), in the following manner: denote the m players by ordered pairs (i, j) where $1 \leq j \leq n$ and $1 \leq i \leq m_j$. Then a coalition S is winning if and only if it contains a subset of the form

$$S' = \bigcup_{j \in T} S_j \times \{j\}$$

where T is winning in w, and each S_j is winning in v_j. (Heuristically, this suggests a "decomposition" of the game into n committees $M_j \times \{j\}$.)

For $x^j \in V_j$ and $y \in W$, let z be the m-vector with components $z_{ij} = x_i^j y_j$. Show that the set of all such z is a stable set solution of the "compound" simple game u.

7. Let v be a simple game for a denumerable infinity of players, for which a set is winning if and only if its complement is finite.

If v is in (0, 1) normalization, the set $E(v)$ consists of all sequences $(x_1, x_2, \ldots)$ of non-negative numbers such that $\sum x_i = 1$.

Then v has no stable set solutions. (Show that no imputation can belong to a stable set.)

8. Let v be the simple four-person game in (0, 1) normalization with winning coalitions $\{1, 2, 4\}$ $\{1, 3, 4\}$ $\{2, 3, 4\}$ and $\{1, 2, 3, 4\}$. Let C be any closed subset of $[0, 1)$, and let J be the set of all vectors $x = \left(0, \frac{1-u}{2}, \frac{1-u}{2}, u\right)$ for $u \in C$. Then v has a stable set solution V, such that $J \subset V$, and the two sets J, $V - J$ are closed and disjoint (and therefore separated).
   (a) Let $\rho(u, C) = \min_{v \in C} |u - v|$. Then let K be the set of all imputations of the form

$$\left(\frac{1 - u - \rho(u, C)}{2}, x, y, u\right)$$

   for all $u \in [0, 1]$. Show K is closed and $K \cap J = \varnothing$.
   (b) Let H consist of all those imputations in K which are dominated by some imputation in J. Then

$$V = J \cup (K - H)$$

   is the desired stable set.

9. Prove Theorem VIII.5.4.

CHAPTER IX

OTHER SOLUTION CONCEPTS FOR *n*-PERSON GAMES

IX.1 THE SHAPLEY VALUE

The fact that no general existence theorem has been given for n-person games has led mathematicians to look for other solution concepts. One such concept is the Shapley value.

Shapley approaches his value axiomatically. We give two definitions first.

IX.1.1 Definition. A *carrier* for a game v is a coalition, T, such that, for any S, $v(S) = v(S \cap T)$.

Intuitively, Definition IX.1.1 states that any player who does not belong to a carrier is a dummy—i.e., can contribute nothing to any coalition.

IX.1.2 Definition. Let v be an n-person game, and let π be any permutation of the set N. Then, by πv, we mean the game u

such that, for any $S = \{i_1, i_2, \ldots, i_s\}$,

$$u(\{\pi(i_1), \pi(i_2), \ldots, \pi(i_s)\}) = v(S).$$

Effectively, the game πv is nothing other than the game v, with the roles of the players interchanged by the permutation π.

With these two definitions, it is possible to give an axiomatic treatment. We point out merely that, as games are essentially real-valued functions, it is possible to talk of the sum of two or more games, or of a number times a game.

IX.1.3 Axioms (Shapley). By the value of a game v, we shall mean an n-vector, $\varphi[v]$, satisfying:

S1. If S is any carrier of S, then

$$\sum_S \varphi_i[v] = v(S)$$

S2. For any permutation π, and $i \in N$,

$$\varphi_{\pi(i)}[\pi v] = \varphi_i[v]$$

S3. If u and v are any games,

$$\varphi_i[u + v] = \varphi_i[u] + \varphi_i[v].$$

These are Shapley's axioms. It is a remarkable fact that these axioms are sufficient to determine a value, φ, uniquely, for all games.

IX.1.4 Theorem. There is a unique function, φ, defined on all games, satisfying Axioms S1–S3.

The proof of IX.1.4 is given by the following sequence of lemmata.

IX.1.5 Lemma. For any coalition S, let the game w_S be defined by

$$w_S(T) = \begin{cases} 0 & \text{if } S \not\subset T \\ 1 & \text{if } S \subset T. \end{cases}$$

Then, if s is the number of players in S,

$$\varphi_i[w_S] = \begin{cases} \dfrac{1}{s} & \text{if } i \in S \\ 0 & \text{if } i \notin S. \end{cases}$$

PROOF: It is clear that S is a carrier for w_S, as is any superset T of S. By Axiom S2, then, it follows that

$$\sum_T \varphi_i[w_S] = 1 \quad \text{if } S \subset T.$$

But this means (as $S = T$ is also a possibility) that $\varphi_i[w_S] = 0$ for $i \notin S$.

Now, if π is any permutation which carries S into itself, it is clear that $\pi w_S = w_S$. Hence, by S2, $\varphi_i[w_S] = \varphi_j[w_S]$ for any $i, j \in S$. As there are s of these terms, and their sum is 1, it follows that $\varphi_i[w_S] = 1/s$ if $i \in S$.

IX.1.6 Corollary. If $c > 0$, then

$$\varphi_i[cw_S] = \begin{cases} c/s & \text{if } i \in S \\ 0 & \text{if } i \notin S. \end{cases}$$

IX.1.7 Lemma. If v is any game, then there exist $2^n - 1$ real numbers, c_S, for $S \subset N$, such that

$$v = \sum_{S \subset N} c_S w_S$$

where w_S is as in IX.1.5.

PROOF: Let

9.1.1 $$c_S = \sum_{T \subset S} (-1)^{s-t} v(T)$$

(where t is the number of elements in T). We shall show that these c_S satisfy the lemma. In fact, if U is any coalition,

$$\begin{aligned} \sum_{S \subset N} c_S w_S(U) &= \sum_{S \subset U} c_S \\ &= \sum_{S \subset U} \left(\sum_{T \subset S} (-1)^{s-t} v(T) \right) \\ &= \sum_{T \subset U} \left(\sum_{\substack{S \subset U \\ S \supset T}} (-1)^{s-t} \right) v(T). \end{aligned}$$

Now, consider the inner parenthesis in this last expression. For every value of s between t and u, there will be $\binom{u-t}{u-s}$ sets S with s elements such that $T \subset S \subset U$. Hence the inner parenthesis may be replaced by

$$\sum_{s=t}^{u} \binom{u - t}{u - s} (-1)^{s-t}.$$

But this is precisely the binomial expansion of $(1 - 1)^{u-t}$. Hence this will be zero for all $t < u$, and 1 for $t = u$. Hence we have

$$\sum_{S \subset N} c_S w_S(U) = v(U)$$

for all $U \subset N$.

We can now proceed to prove Theorem IX.1.4. In fact, Lemma IX.1.7 shows that any game can be written as a linear combination of games w_S. By Lemma IX.1.5, the function φ is uniquely defined for such games. Now, some of the coefficients c_S are negative; however, it is easy to see from Axiom S3 that if u, v and $u - v$ are all games, then $\varphi[u - v] = \varphi[u] - \varphi[v]$. By S3, then, the function φ is uniquely defined for all games v. We can also give the exact form of the function φ. We know that

$$v = \sum_{S \subset N} c_S w_S$$

and so

$$\varphi_i[v] = \sum_{S \subset N} c_S \varphi_i[w_S]$$

$$= \sum_{\substack{S \subset N \\ i \in S}} c_S \cdot \frac{1}{s}.$$

But c_S is defined by 9.1.1, above; substituting this here, we obtain

$$\varphi_i[v] = \sum_{\substack{S \subset N \\ i \in S}} \frac{1}{s} \left\{ \sum_{T \subset S} (-1)^{s-t} v(T) \right\}$$

$$\textbf{9.1.2} \quad \varphi_i[v] = \sum_{T \subset N} \left\{ \sum_{\substack{S \subset N \\ T \cup \{i\} \subset S}} (-1)^{s-t} \frac{1}{s} v(T) \right\}.$$

From 9.1.2, let us write

$$\textbf{9.1.3} \quad \gamma_i(T) = \sum_{\substack{S \subset N \\ T \cup \{i\} \subset S}} (-1)^{s-t} \frac{1}{s}.$$

It is easy to see that, if $i \notin T'$ and $T = T' \cup \{i\}$, then $\gamma_i(T') = -\gamma_i(T)$. In fact, all the terms in the right side of 9.1.3 will be the same in both cases, except that $t = t' + 1$, and so there is a change of sign throughout. This means we will have

$$\varphi_i[v] = \sum_{\substack{T \subset N \\ i \in T}} \gamma_i(T)\{v(T) - v(T - \{i\})\}.$$

Now, if $i \in T$, we see there are exactly $\binom{n-t}{s-t}$ coalitions S with s elements such that $T \subset S$. Thus we have

$$\begin{aligned}
\gamma_i(T) &= \sum_{s=t}^{n} (-1)^{s-t}\binom{n-t}{s-t}\frac{1}{s} \\
&= \sum_{s=t}^{n} (-1)^{s-t}\binom{n-t}{s-t}\int_0^1 x^{s-1}\,dx \\
&= \int_0^1 \sum_{s=t}^{n} (-1)^{s-t}\binom{n-t}{s-t}x^{s-1}\,dx \\
&= \int_0^1 x^{t-1}\sum_{s=t}^{n} (-1)^{s-t}\binom{n-t}{s-t}x^{s-t}\,dx \\
&= \int_0^1 x^{t-1}(1-x)^{n-t}\,dx.
\end{aligned}$$

But this is a well-known definite integral; we have, thus,

$$\gamma_i(T) = \frac{(t-1)!\,(n-t)!}{n!}$$

and thus

$$\textbf{9.1.4} \quad \varphi_i[v] = \sum_{\substack{T \subset N \\ i \in T}} \frac{(t-1)!\,(n-t)!}{n!}\,[v(T) - v(T - \{i\})].$$

Formula 9.1.4 gives the Shapley value, explicitly. It is then easy to check that this expression will satisfy Axioms S1–S3. Moreover, it can be seen that the sum of the coefficients $\gamma_i(T)$ is equal to 1. For the numerator is equal to the number of permutations of N in which i is preceded exactly by the elements of T, while the numerator is the total number of permutations. By super-additivity, the bracket is always at least equal to $v(\{i\})$. Hence we see that

$$\textbf{9.1.5} \quad \varphi_i[v] \geq v(\{i\})$$

and so $\varphi[v]$ is always an imputation.

Apart from the axiomatic treatment, the Shapley value, as defined by 9.1.4, can be given the following heuristic explanation: Suppose the players (the elements of N) agree to meet at a specified place and time. Naturally, because of random fluctuations, all will arrive at different times; it is assumed, however, that all orders of arrival (permutations of the players) have the same probability: viz., $1/n!$. Suppose that, if a player, i, arrives, and finds the members of the coalition $T - \{i\}$ (and no others) already there, he receives the amount $v(T) - v(T - \{i\})$: i.e., the marginal amount which he contributes to the coalition, as payoff. Then the Shapley value, $\varphi_i[v]$, is the expected payoff to player i under this randomization scheme.

In case the game v is simple, the formula for the Shapley value becomes especially simple. In fact, the term $v(T) - v(T - \{i\})$ will always have value 0 or 1, taking the value 1 whenever T is a winning coalition but $T - \{i\}$ is not. Hence we would have

$$\varphi_i[v] = \sum_T \frac{(t-1)!\,(n-t)!}{n!}$$

where the summation is taken over all winning coalitions T such that $T - \{1\}$ is not winning.

IX.1.6 Example. Consider a corporation with four stockholders, having respectively 10, 20, 30, and 40 shares of stock. It is assumed that any decision can be settled by approval of stockholders holding a simple majority of the shares. This can be treated as a simple four-person game, in which the winning coalitions are: {2, 4}, {3, 4}, {1, 2, 3}, {1, 2, 4}, {1, 3, 4}, {2, 3, 4}, and {1, 2, 3, 4}. We would like to find the Shapley value of this game.

To find φ_1, we note that the only winning coalition, T, such that $T - \{1\}$ is not winning, is {1, 2, 3}. Hence, as $t = 3$,

$$\varphi_1 = \frac{2!\,1!}{4!} = \frac{1}{12}.$$

Similarly, we find that {2, 4}, {1, 2, 3}, and {2, 3, 4} are winning coalitions which are not winning if 2 is removed. Hence

$$\varphi_2 = \tfrac{1}{12} + \tfrac{1}{12} + \tfrac{1}{12} = \tfrac{1}{4}.$$

In the same way, we find $\varphi_3 = \frac{1}{4}$, while $\varphi_4 = \frac{5}{12}$. Thus the

Shapley value is the vector $(\frac{1}{12}, \frac{1}{4}, \frac{1}{4}, \frac{5}{12})$. This contrasts with the "vote vector," which would be $(\frac{1}{10}, \frac{1}{5}, \frac{3}{10}, \frac{2}{5})$. Note that the value is the same for players 2 and 3, even though player 3 has many more shares. This is not surprising, since player 3 has no greater opportunity than 2 to form a winning coalition; the game (thought of as a characteristic function) treats these two players symmetrically.

In a similar way, it is clear that player 4's strength is greater than his share of the stock, while player 1's strength is less.

IX.1.7 Example. Consider a game similar to that of Example IX.1.6, except that the players have 10, 30, 30, and 40 shares respectively. It may be seen that any two of players 2, 3, 4 form a winning coalition, while player 1 is a dummy: he cannot contribute anything to any coalition. Thus the value vector is $(0, \frac{1}{3}, \frac{1}{3}, \frac{1}{3})$: player 1's shares are useless, while player 4's extra shares give him no advantage over players 2 and 3.

IX.2 THE BARGAINING SET

One of the difficulties with the concepts which we have previously studied is that, in general, they do not seem to explain what happens in any play of the game. Stable sets are given as "standards of behavior"; the Shapley value gives some type of expectation. The *bargaining set* is obtained by considering the discussion that may actually take place during a play of the game. Thus we shall consider the possible threats and counter-threats made by the several players.

IX.2.1 Definition. By a *coalition structure* for an n-person game we mean a partition

$$\mathscr{T} = \{T_1, T_2, \ldots, T_m\}$$

of N.

Heuristically, a coalition structure represents the "breaking up" of the set N into mutually disjoint coalitions. Suppose such a structure is reached. We assume that each of the coalitions T_k which forms will receive the amount $v(T_k)$ to be divided among its members. But how will this amount be divided?

IX.2.2 Definition. A *payoff configuration* is a pair

$$(x; \mathscr{T}) = (x_1, \ldots, x_n; T_1, \ldots, T_m)$$

where $\mathscr{T}$ is a coalition structure and x is an n-vector satisfying

9.2.1 $\sum_{i \in T_k} x_i = v(T_k)$

for $k = 1, \ldots, m$.

We wish, then, to know which payoff configurations will be reached. An obvious requirement will be that of individual rationality: i.e., we may demand

9.2.2 $x_i \geq v(\{i\})$ for all $i \in N$.

A further possible requirement may be that no coalition T_k will form if one of its subcoalitions can obtain more than the payoff vector x gives it. Thus

9.2.3 $\sum_{i \in S} x_i \geq v(S)$ for $S \subset T_k \in \mathscr{T}$.

It is clear, of course, that 9.2.3 is stronger than 9.2.2. On the other hand, the necessity for 9.2.3 is not as clear as that for 9.2.2. Without going into the pros and cons of 9.2.3, we shall merely say here that a payoff configuration satisfying 9.2.3 will be called *coalitionally rational* (c.r.p.c.) whereas if it satisfies only 9.2.2 it will be called *individually rational* (i.r.p.c.). We shall deal, first of all, with c.r.p.c.'s.

Suppose, then, that some c.r.p.c. has been reached. When will this be stable? It is clear that if the c.r.p.c. is an imputation in the core of the game, it will be stable in the sense that no coalition has both the power and inclination to change it. Since, however, the core is often empty, it follows that we cannot be as demanding as this.

Consider, for example, the symmetric three-person game previously treated. If the coalition $\{1, 2\}$ forms, we saw that the payoff vector $(\frac{1}{2}, \frac{1}{2}, 0)$ is quite likely. Nevertheless, either of the two players in the coalition might demand more of the other, and threaten to join player 3 if his demand is not met. Thus player 1 might threaten to form the coalition $\{1, 3\}$, obtaining, say, the payoff $(\frac{3}{4}, 0, \frac{1}{4})$. Player 2, however, can counter this threat by pointing out that, in such a case, he will try to form the coalition $\{2, 3\}$, offering 3 the amount $\frac{1}{2}$, to obtain the vector $(0, \frac{1}{2}, \frac{1}{2})$. Thus player 2 has a counter-threat which "protects" his share of $\frac{1}{2}$.

To formulate this idea mathematically, we begin by defining the idea of partners.

IX.2.3 Definition. Let $\mathscr{T} = \{T_1, \ldots, T_m\}$ be a coalition structure, and let K be a coalition. Then, by *the partners* of K in $\mathscr{T}$, we mean the set

$$P(K; \mathscr{T}) = \{i \mid i \in T_k, \; T_k \cap K \neq \varnothing\}.$$

Thus the player i is a partner of K in $\mathscr{T}$ if he belongs to the same coalition T_k as some member of K. (Note that each member of K is also a partner of K.) The idea is that, for the members of K to get their share of the c.r.p.c. $(x; \mathscr{T})$, they need the consent of their partners and no other.

IX.2.4 Definition. Let $(x; \mathscr{T})$ be a c.r.p.c. for a game v. Let K and L be non-empty disjoint subsets of some $T_k \in \mathscr{T}$. Then an *objection* of K against L is a c.r.p.c. $(y; \mathscr{U})$, satisfying

9.2.4 $P(K; \mathscr{U}) \cap L = \varnothing$

9.2.5 $y_i > x_i$ for all $i \in K$

9.2.6 $y_i \geq x_i$ for all $i \in P(K; \mathscr{U})$.

IX.2.5 Definition. Let $(x; \mathscr{T})$ be a c.r.p.c., let K, L be as in Definition IX.2.4, and let $(y; \mathscr{U})$ be an objection of K against L. Then a *counter-objection* of L against K is a c.r.p.c. $(z; \mathscr{V})$, satisfying

9.2.7 $K \not\subset P(L; \mathscr{V})$

9.2.8 $z_i \geq x_i$ for $i \in P(L; \mathscr{V})$

9.2.9 $z_i \geq y_i$ for $i \in P(L; \mathscr{V}) \cap P(K; \mathscr{U})$.

Briefly, the members of K, in their objection against L, claim that they can obtain more by changing to a new c.r.p.c., and that their new partners will agree to this. The members of L can counter-object if it is possible for them to find a third c.r.p.c. in which they and all their partners receive at least their original shares. If they need some of K's partners for this, they give these players at least as much as in the objection c.r.p.c. Note that it may be necessary for L to use some members of K as partners; they may not, however, use them all.

IX.2.6 Definition. A c.r.p.c. $(x; \mathscr{T})$ is called *stable* if for every objection of a K against an L, L has a counter-objection. The *bargaining set* $\mathscr{M}$ is the set of all stable c.r.p.c.'s.

Now, the form of the bargaining set is open to some question. Certain modifications might, indeed, be made. For example, we might insist that only single players be allowed to make objections, or that it should be sufficient for one member of L to possess a counter-objection.

IX.2.7 Definition. The bargaining set $\mathscr{M}_1$ is the set of all c.r.p.c.'s $(x; \mathscr{T})$ such that, whenever any set K has an objection against a set L, at least one member of L has a counter-objection.

IX.2.8 Definition. The bargaining set $\mathscr{M}_2$ is the set of all c.r.p.c.'s $(x; \mathscr{T})$ such that, if any single player, i, has an objection against a set L, then L has a counter-objection against i.

It is easy to see that $\mathscr{M} \subset \mathscr{M}_1$ and $\mathscr{M} \subset \mathscr{M}_2$. The relationship between $\mathscr{M}_1$ and $\mathscr{M}_2$ is not clear.

One final variation might be suggested for the bargaining set. It is that, instead of c.r.p.c.'s, we deal with i.r.p.c.'s. This will give rise to the three sets, $\mathscr{M}^{(i)}$, $\mathscr{M}_1^{(i)}$, $\mathscr{M}_2^{(i)}$, derived from $\mathscr{M}$, $\mathscr{M}_1$, $\mathscr{M}_2$ respectively.

In contrast with the core, which is so often empty, it may be seen that none of the bargaining sets mentioned above is empty. In fact (assuming the game to be in (0, 1) normalization) the c.r.p.c. $(x; \mathscr{T})$, where $x = (0, 0, \ldots, 0)$ and $\mathscr{T} = \{\{1\}, \{2\}, \ldots, \{n\}\}$, is obviously stable. On the other hand, it represents complete failure to cooperate. Thus we would like to find elements in the bargaining set for some of the more interesting coalition structures. We have, in fact, the following valuable result:

IX.2.9 Theorem. Let v be an n-person game, and let $\mathscr{T}$ be any coalition structure. Then there is at least one vector x such that $(x; \mathscr{T}) \in \mathscr{M}_1^{(i)}$.

We shall assume the game is in (0, 1) normalization. For a given coalition structure, $\mathscr{T}$, we shall let $X(\mathscr{T})$ denote the set of all vectors x such that $(x; \mathscr{T})$ is an i.r.p.c. The following lemma is that of B. Peleg:

IX.2.10 Lemma. Let $c_1(x), c_2(x), \ldots, c_n(x)$ be non-negative continuous real-valued functions defined for $x \in X(\mathscr{T})$. If, for each $x \in X(\mathscr{T})$, and each $S_j \in \mathscr{T}$, there is a player $i \in S_j$ such that $c_i(x) \geq x_i$, then there exists a point $\xi = (\xi_1, \ldots, \xi_n) \in X(\mathscr{T})$ such that $c_i(\xi) \geq \xi_i$ for $i = 1, 2, \ldots, n$.

PROOF OF LEMMA: For $x \in X(\mathscr{T})$, and $i \in N$, we denote

$$d_i = \begin{cases} x_i - c_i(x) & \text{if } x_i \geq c_i(x) \\ 0 & \text{if } x_i \leq c_i(x) \end{cases}$$

and, if $i \in S_j$,

$$y_i = x_i - d_i + \frac{1}{s_j} \sum_{k \in S_j} d_k$$

where s_j is the number of elements in S_j.

It is clear that y is a continuous function of x. Moreover, we can see that $y_i \geq 0$ as x_i, d_i and $c_i(x)$ are all non-negative. Finally, we have

$$\sum_{i \in S_j} y_i = \sum_{i \in S_j} x_i = v(S_j)$$

and so $y \in X(\mathscr{T})$.

Suppose now that $x_i > c_i(x)$. This means $d_i > 0$. However, the hypothesis is that, for some $k \in S_j$, $x_k \leq c_k(x)$, and so $d_k = 0$. Hence

$$y_k \geq x_k + \frac{d_i}{s_j} > x_k$$

and so x is not fixed under this mapping. As $X(\mathscr{T})$ is convex, however, the Brouwer fixed point theorem applies, and so there must be some ξ such that $y(\xi) = \xi$. We have just seen that this ξ must satisfy $\xi_i \leq c_i(\xi)$ for all $i = 1, 2, \ldots, n$.

IX.2.11 Definition. We shall say a player i is *stronger* than k in $(x; \mathscr{T})$ if i has an objection against k which cannot be countered. We denote this $i \gg k$. We say i and k are *equal*, denoted $i \sim k$, if neither $i \gg k$ nor $k \gg i$.

IX.2.12 Definition. Let $(x; \mathscr{T})$ be an i.r.p.c., and let C be a coalition. Then the *excess* of C is $e(C) = v(C) - \sum_{i \in C} x_i$.

IX.2.13 Lemma. Let $(x; \mathscr{T})$ be an i.r.p.c. Then the relation $\gg$ is acyclic.

PROOF: It is clear that if i and k are in different coalitions, then $i \sim k$. Suppose, then, that a coalition, S_j, contains the players $1, 2, \ldots, t$, and that $1 \gg 2 \gg 3 \gg \cdots \gg t \gg 1$. Thus player i $(i = 1, \ldots, t)$ has an objection, which cannot be countered, against player $i + 1 \pmod t$ through the coalition C_i. Let C_{i_0} be that coalition (among $C_1, C_2, \ldots, C_t$) which has maximal excess. Then we claim that i_0 can counter-object against $i_0 - 1 \pmod t$ through the coalition C_{i_0}. Indeed, $i_0 - 1$ (mod t) has only the amount $e(C_{i_0-1})$ at his disposal to form the objecting coalition; player i_0, having the amount $e(C_{i_0}) \geq e(C_{i_0-1})$ at his disposal, can always counter-object unless $i_0 - 1 \pmod t \in C_{i_0}$. Repeating this argument, we must have $i_0 - 2 \pmod t \in C_{i_0}$, etc., and eventually $i_0 + 1 \pmod t \in C_{i_0}$. But this is obviously impossible.

IX.2.14 Proof of Theorem IX.2.9: Let $(x; \mathscr{T})$ be an i.r.p.c. We shall denote by $(y^{S_j}, x^{N-S_j}; \mathscr{T})$ the i.r.p.c. which is obtained by keeping x_i fixed for $i \in N - S_j$, and replacing x_k by y_k for $k \in S_j$, where $y_k \geq 0$ and $\sum_{k \in S_j} y_k = v(S_j)$.

Let $E_j^i(x)$ be the set of points y^{S_j} such that, in the i.r.p.c. $(y^{S_j}, x^{N-S_j}; T)$, player i $(i \in S_j)$ is *not weaker* than any other player. The set $E_j^i(x)$ is closed and contains the set $x_i = 0$ (since, if $x_i = 0$, i can always counter-object as a one-player coalition). We then define the function

$$C_i(x) = x_i + \max_{y^{S_j} \in E_j^i(x)} \ \min_{k \in S_j} (x_k - y_k)$$

where S_j is the coalition in T which contains i. Now, $C_i(x)$ is easily seen to be continuous; moreover, it is non-negative, as can be seen by showing that if $y_i = 0$, and $y_k \geq x_k$ for all $k \in S_j$, $k \neq i$, then $y^{S_j} \in E_j^i(x)$.

By Lemma IX.2.13, for any $x \in X(\mathscr{T})$ and any $S_j \in \mathscr{T}$, there is some $i \in S_j$ such that i is *not weaker* than any $k \in S_j$. Thus, $x^{S_j} \in E_j^i(x)$, and so $C_i(x) \geq x_i$. Hence, by Lemma IX.2.10, there is some ξ such that $C_i(\xi) \geq \xi_i$ for all $i \in N$.

Now it is clear from the fact that

$$\sum_{k \in S_j} x_k = \sum_{k \in S_j} y_k$$

that $c_i(x) \leq x_i$ for all i. Hence, we actually have $c_i(\xi) = \xi_i$ for all i. But this means that there is some $y \in E_j^i(\xi)$, for each i, such that $y_k = \xi_k$. But this in turn means $\xi^{S_j} \in E^i_j(\xi)$ for each i and j. Thus, in $(\xi; \mathscr{T})$, *no player is stronger than another.* This means, of course, that $(\xi; \mathscr{T}) \in \mathscr{M}_1^{(i)}$.

IX.2.15 Example. Consider the five-person simple game in (0, 1) normalization in which the minimal winning coalitions are {1, 2}, {1, 3}, {1, 4}, {1, 5}, and {2, 3, 4, 5}. We shall consider two types of coalition structures: one in which {1, 2} forms, and a second one in which {2, 3, 4, 5} forms.

Suppose that {1, 2} forms. It does not matter what the other players do, but we shall assume they do not form any coalition. Hence $\mathscr{T} = \{\{1, 2\}, \{3\}, \{4\}, \{5\}\}$. The i.r.p.c.'s will consist of all $(x; \mathscr{T})$ where x is a vector with $x_1 + x_2 = 1$, $x_3 = x_4 = x_5 = 0$, $x_1 \geq 0$, $x_2 \geq 0$. Now, if $x_1 > \frac{3}{4}$, we must have $x_2 < \frac{1}{4}$, and so player 2 can object with the imputation $(0, \frac{1}{4}, \frac{1}{4}, \frac{1}{4}, \frac{1}{4})$. It is easy to see that 1 will have no counter-objection. If, on the other hand, $x_1 \leq \frac{3}{4}$, we find that any objection of 2 will give one of his partners an amount smaller than $\frac{1}{4}$. Say $x_3 < \frac{1}{4}$. Then 1 can counter-object with $(\frac{3}{4}, 0, \frac{1}{4}, 0, 0)$. Similarly, if $x_1 < \frac{1}{2}$, then 1 can object with, say, $(\frac{1}{2}, 0, \frac{1}{2}, 0, 0)$, and 2 has no counter-objection. But if $x_1 \geq \frac{1}{2}$, then any objection y by 1 will give the players 3, 4, 5 a total of less than $\frac{1}{2}$. Thus 2 can counter-object with $z = (0, \frac{1}{2}, y_3 + \varepsilon_3, y_4 + \varepsilon_4, y_5 + \varepsilon_5)$. Thus, for the given $\mathscr{T}$, $(x; \mathscr{T})$ will belong to $\mathscr{M}_1^{(i)}$ if and only if x satisfies

9.2.10 $x_1 + x_2 = 1$

9.2.11 $x_1 \geq \frac{1}{2}$

9.2.12 $x_2 \geq \frac{1}{4}$

9.2.13 $x_3 = x_4 = x_5 = 0.$

By symmetry, similar results will hold if the coalitions {1, 3}, {1, 4}, or {1, 5} form.

Suppose, instead, that the coalition {2, 3, 4, 5} forms. We must consider all i.r.p.c.'s $(x; \mathscr{T})$ where x is a non-negative vector of sum 1 with $x_1 = 0$, and $\mathscr{T} = \{\{1\}, \{2, 3, 4, 5\}\}$. Suppose we have $x_2 > x_3$. Then 3 can object against 2 with the imputation $(1 - x_3 - \varepsilon, 0, x_3 + \varepsilon, 0, 0)$ where $0 < \varepsilon < x_2 - x_3$. It is easy to see that 2 has no counter-objection. By symmetry, it follows that the only x such that $(x; \mathscr{T}) \in \mathscr{M}_1^{(i)}$ for this $\mathscr{T}$ is

9.2.14 $x_1 = 0$

9.2.15 $x_2 = x_3 = x_4 = x_5 = \frac{1}{4}.$

IX.3 ψ-STABILITY

A somewhat different view of the bargaining process gives rise to the concept of ψ-stability. As in the bargaining set, an outcome is a pair $(x; \mathscr{T})$ where x is a payoff vector and $\mathscr{T}$ is a coalition structure. However, the idea behind ψ-stability is considerably simpler; briefly, objections are considered, but there is no worry about counter-objections. Since this would tend to leave the set of stable outcomes much too small (empty except for the core), we decrease the number of objections by noting that only certain coalitions can object to a given outcome.

In mathematical terms, a function ψ is given which will assign, to each partition of N, a collection of subsets of N. Thus if $\mathscr{T}$ is a partition, $\psi(\mathscr{T})$ is a collection of coalitions. Heuristically, $S \in \psi(\mathscr{T})$ if and only if the disrupting coalition S is allowed to form from the present coalition structure $\mathscr{T}$.

IX.3.1 Definition. Let ψ be a function, which assigns to each partition $\mathscr{T}$ a collection of coalitions. Then the pair $(x; T)$, where x is an imputation, will be said to be ψ-stable if and only if:

$$\text{(i)} \quad \text{for all } S \in \psi(\mathscr{T}),\ \sum_{i \in S} x_i \geq v(S)$$

$$\text{(ii)} \quad x_i > v(\{i\}) \quad \text{unless } \{i\} \in \mathscr{T}$$

Condition (i) states, of course, that none of the "permissible" coalitions is capable of disrupting $(x; \mathscr{T})$. Condition (ii) states that no player will join a non-trivial coalition unless he receives more than his minimax value, $v(\{i\})$.

Generally, the principal difficulty with ψ-stability is that of deciding upon a reasonable function, ψ. If ψ is restrictive enough, there will be many stable pairs. But if ψ is not too restrictive, it may turn out that there are no stable pairs, or that only the core is ψ-stable. Thus, not too much work has been done on ψ-stability.

One "reasonable" possibility for ψ would be what is called k-stability, where k is a positive integer. In this case, ψ is defined by saying that $S \in \psi(\mathscr{T})$ if and only if there is a $T \in \mathscr{T}$ such that $S \Delta T = (S - T) \cup (T - S)$ has not more than k elements. For such functions ψ, we give the following results without proof:

IX.3.2 Theorem. Any constant-sum n-person game is $(n-2)$-unstable: i.e., the set of $(n-2)$-stable pairs is empty.

IX.3.3 Definition. An n-person game v is said to be a *quota* game if there exists a vector $\omega = (\omega_1, \ldots, \omega_n)$ such that $\sum \omega_i = v(N)$, and for any $i, j \in N$, $i \neq j$, $v(\{i, j\}) = \omega_i + \omega_j$. A player i in a quota game is *weak* if $\omega_i < v(\{i\})$.

It is easy to see that a quota game has at most one weak player, as $v(\{i, j\}) \geq v(\{i\}) + v(\{j\})$. Then

IX.3.4 Theorem. Let $(x; \mathcal{T})$ be a k-stable pair for an n-person quota game. Then, if n is odd, or if n is even and $k \geq 2$, we must have $x = \omega$. If n is even and $k = 1$, then each $T \in \mathcal{T}$ will have an even number of elements and, moreover,

$$\sum_{i \in T} x_i = \sum_{i \in T} \omega_i.$$

Finally, a quota game with a weak player is k-unstable for any k.

PROBLEMS

1. If v is a constant-sum game, then the Shapley value φ is given by

$$\varphi_i[v] = 2 \sum_{\substack{S \subset N \\ i \in S}} \left[\frac{(n-s)!\,(s-1)!}{n!} v(S) \right] - v(N)$$

2. An *m-quota game for n persons* is a game v, such that a vector $\omega = (\omega_1, \ldots, \omega_n)$ exists satisfying $\sum_{i \in N} \omega_i = v(N)$, and for each m-person coalition $M \subset N$, $\sum_{i \in M} \omega_i = v(M)$, while, for an s-person coalition S, $(s \neq m)$, $v(S) = \sum_{i \in S} v(\{i\})$. Player i is said to be weak if $\omega_i < v(\{i\})$. A coalition structure $\mathcal{T}$ for such a game is a *maximal coalition structure* (m.c.s.) if it contains the largest possible number $\left(\text{i.e., } \left[\frac{n}{m}\right]\right)$ of m-person coalitions.

   (a) Let v be an m-quota game, with quota ω, and no weak players. If T is a m.c.s., then the c.r.p.c. $(x; \mathcal{T})$ is in the bargaining set $\mathcal{M}_0$ if and only if $x_i = w_i$ for all i belonging to an m-player coalition in $\mathcal{T}$.

(b) Let v be an m-quota game, with quota ω, and let R be the set of weak players. If $n = qm + r$, with $0 \leq r < m$ and $q \geq m + 1$, and if $\mathcal{T}$ is a m.c.s., then the c.r.p.c. $(x; \mathcal{T})$ is in $\mathcal{M}_0$ if and only if $x_i = v(\{i\})$ for all $i \in A$, and $x_i \leq \omega_i$ for $i \in N - A$ (where A is the set of weak players).

3. For an n-person game v, and an i.r.p.c. $(x; \mathcal{T})$ we say that the maximum surplus of i against j (denoted s_{ij}) is

$$s_{ij} = \max_D e(D)$$

where $e(D)$ is the *excess* of D and the maximum is taken over all coalitions D such that $i \in D$ but $j \notin D$. A player i is said to *outweigh* j if $s_{ij} > s_{ji}$ and $x_j > v(\{j\})$. Two players i and j are said to be in equilibrium if neither outweighs the other.

The kernel $\mathcal{K}$ is the set of all i.r.p.c.'s $(x; \mathcal{T})$ such that any two players belonging to the same coalition are in equilibrium.

(a) For any coalition structure $\mathcal{T}$, there is some x such that $(x; \mathcal{T}) \in \mathcal{K}$.

(b) $\mathcal{K} \subset \mathcal{M}_1^{(i)}$.

(c) If v is a simple game, and $\mathcal{T}$ is of the form $\{S, T_1, \ldots, T_l\}$ where S is a minimal winning coalition, then $(x; \mathcal{T}) \in \mathcal{K}$ if and only if, for $i \in S$,

$$x_i = \frac{v(S) - \sum_{j \in S} v(\{j\})}{s} + v(\{i\})$$

(where s is the number of elements in S).

4. Prove Theorem IX.3.2.

5. Prove Theorem IX.3.4.

6. Prove that every four-person constant-sum game is a quota game. Find all k-stable pairs, where $k = 1, 2, 3$.

7. Let v be the same as in Problem VIII.7. Show that, for any non-trivial coalition structure T, the set of all x such that $(x; \mathcal{T}) \in \mathcal{K}$ is empty, whereas the set of all x such that $(x; \mathcal{T}) \in \mathcal{M}_1^{(i)}$ is non-empty.

CHAPTER X

MODIFICATIONS OF THE GAME CONCEPT

X.1 GAMES WITH A CONTINUUM OF PLAYERS

In the attempt to apply n-person game theory to economic analysis, it becomes quite clear that small games (i.e., games with a small number of players) are hardly adequate to represent free-market situations. We want, for this purpose, games with such a large number of players that any single player will have a negligible effect on the payoffs to the other players. How large a number should this be? As large as the number of points on a line. (Generally, this line will be the unit interval, [0, 1].) This can best be defined as follows.

X.1.1 Definition. By a *game for a continuum of players* we shall mean a σ-algebra, ϑ, of subsets of [0, 1], together with a real-valued function, v, defined on ϑ, satisfying

(i) $v(\varnothing) = 0$

(ii) $v(A \cup B) \geq v(A) + v(B) \quad \text{if } A \cap B = \varnothing.$

As before, we point out that the elements of ϑ are called coalitions, while the elements of [0, 1] are called players.

One must tread more carefully here than in the case of finite games. For example, the definition of (0, 1) normalization must be altered: it is not enough now to demand that $v(\{x\}) = 0$ for any point $x \in [0, 1]$, and $v([0, 1]) = 1$; this would be satisfied by letting v be equal, say, to Lebesgue measure. But a measure is additive, and such a game would therefore be inessential. Instead, we redefine (0, 1) normalization by the conditions

10.1.1 $v([0, 1]) = 1$

10.1.2 $v(S) \geq 0 \quad \text{if } S \in \vartheta$

10.1.3 If α is a measure on ϑ, and $\alpha \leq v$, then $\alpha \equiv 0$.

A restatement of 10.1.3 is given by observing that, if $v \geq 0$, then the set function

10.1.4 $\alpha(S) = \inf \sum v(S_i)$

where the infimum is taken over all sequences of sets S_i, from ϑ, such that $\bigcup S_i \supset S$. This implies that α is an outer measure. But the super-additivity of v means that this infimum is obtained by taking "fine" partitions of the set S, and this means that all elements of ϑ are measurable under α. Thus α is a measure on ϑ. Now, it is easily seen that α is the largest measure such that $\alpha \leq v$. Thus 10.1.3 can be replaced by:

10.1.5 If α is as defined by 10.1.4, then $\alpha \equiv 0$.

It should be pointed out that, even if v is not non-negative, a signed measure α can be defined in a somewhat modified manner.

In general, this measure, or signed measure, α, will replace the numbers $v(\{i\})$. Thus, an imputation for the game v is defined to be any (signed) measure σ, such that

10.1.6 $\sigma([0, 1]) = v([0, 1])$

10.1.7 $\sigma(S) \geq \alpha(S) \quad \text{for } S \in \vartheta.$

If the game is in (0, 1) normalization, of course, condition 10.1.7 is replaced by saying simply that σ must be a measure rather than a signed measure.

The domination relation must also be redefined. In fact, to have $\sigma \succ \tau$ through a set S, the relation $\sigma(S) \leq v(S)$ must certainly hold; it is not possible, however, to demand that $\sigma(A) > \tau(A)$ for all $A \subset S$, as this can certainly not hold if S is non-denumerable and all one-point sets belong to ϑ. On the other hand, it is certainly not sufficient to demand merely $\sigma(A) \geq \tau(A)$ for $A \subset S$, as this might lead to the relation $\sigma \succ \sigma$. We compromise by demanding that the inequality $\sigma(A) > \tau(A)$ must hold for all subsets A of ϑ which are such that

$$\sup_{B \in \vartheta} \{v(A \cup B) - v(B)\} > 0.$$

This effectively allows us to dispense with "small" (e.g., finite) sets.

With these definitions of imputation and domination, stable sets can be defined exactly as for finite games. In general, not much is known about stable sets for such games—just as little is known about stable sets for n-person games, when n is large—except for special types. In particular, stable sets will exist for simple games: if S is a minimal winning coalition, the set of all imputations σ such that $\sigma \equiv 0$ on $[0, 1] - S$ will be stable. (We assume $(0, 1)$ normalization here.)

Although little work has been done on stable sets, much work has been done on the Shapley value of games for a continuum of players.

Generally, the Axioms S1–S3 given in the definition of the Shapley value in Chapter IX can be adapted directly, *mutatis mutandis*. A certain difficulty arises, however, with S2 (the symmetry axiom); the permutations of N which were treated there must here be replaced by $1 - 1$, measurable transformations of $[0, 1]$ into itself. While this might not, at first sight, present any problems, we shall see that it leads to a contradiction in certain degenerate cases.

The actual determination of the value for a particular game, of course, presents considerable difficulty, inasmuch as the formula is not adaptable to the infinite case.

Generally, the method used to determine the value for an arbitrary game is to partition the interval $[0, 1]$ into subsets (not necessarily sub-intervals). These subsets are then treated as single players and the Shapley value for the corresponding finite game is calculated. Finer and finer partitions of $[0, 1]$ are taken, and the Shapley value $\varphi[v]$ (an additive set function rather than a vector) is then defined as the limit of the values for these finite games (if this limit exists).

Let us suppose, now, that there is a measure, μ, defined on ϑ, such that $v(S)$ depends merely on $\mu(S)$. For example, we might have $v(S) = [\mu(S)]^2$. Then, by the symmetry axiom, if $\mu(S) = \mu(T)$, we would have $\varphi[v](S) = \varphi[v](T)$. But as $\varphi[v]$ must be an additive set function, it follows that $\varphi[v]$ must be equal to the measure μ, divided by a constant factor to ensure that $\varphi[v]([0, 1]) = v([0, 1])$.

X.1.2 Example. Let $\lambda(S)$ be Lebesgue measure, and let $\mu(S)$ be given by

$$\mu(S) = 2\int_S x\, dx.$$

Now, if v is a function of λ alone, then $\varphi[v] = \lambda$; similarly, if v is a function of μ alone, then $\varphi[v] = \mu$. Suppose, now, that

10.1.8 $v(S) = \mu(S)\lambda(S)$

for all $S \in \vartheta$. If we write $v_1 = \frac{1}{2}\mu^2$, $v_2 = \frac{1}{2}\lambda^2$, then

$$v_3 = v + v_1 + v_2 = \tfrac{1}{2}(\lambda + \mu)^2.$$

Now, by additivity, we must have

$$\varphi[v] = \varphi[v_3] - \varphi[v_1] - \varphi[v_2].$$

As λ, μ, and $\lambda + \mu$ are measures, the right side of this equation is easy to evaluate. In fact, v_3 depends only on $\lambda + \mu$; as $v_3[0, 1] = 2$ and $[\lambda + \mu]([0, 1]) = 2$ also, then

10.1.9 $\varphi[v_3] = \lambda + \mu.$

Next, v_1 depends only on μ. We have $v_1([0, 1]) = \frac{1}{2}$; hence,

10.1.10 $\varphi[v_1] = \frac{1}{2}\mu$

and similarly,

10.1.11 $\varphi[v_2] = \frac{1}{2}\lambda.$

Putting all these together, we obtain

10.1.12 $\varphi[v] = \frac{1}{2}(\lambda + \mu)$

as the Shapley value of v defined by 10.1.8, above. In a similar way, we can find the Shapley value of any polynomial function of μ and λ, and for that matter, of any finite set of measures.

Let us suppose now, however, that v is given by

$$v(S) = \begin{cases} 0 & \text{if } \lambda(S) < 1 \\ 1 & \text{if } \lambda(S) = 1. \end{cases}$$

Clearly, here, v is a function of λ, and so we must have $\varphi[v] = \lambda$. It is easy to see, however, that $\mu(S) = 1$ if and only if $\lambda(S) = 1$. Thus we will also have

$$v(S) = \begin{cases} 0 & \text{if} \quad \mu(S) < 1 \\ 1 & \text{if} \quad \mu(S) = 1 \end{cases}$$

and so we must have $\varphi[v] = \mu$. This contradiction shows that the Shapley value $\varphi[v]$ cannot exist for this game. What has happened is that the infinite process described above does not have a limit.

X.2 GAMES WITHOUT SIDE PAYMENTS

Another possible generalization of the games treated in Chapters VIII and IX lies in the area of games without side payments.

Essentially, we have assumed, throughout these two chapters, that utility can be linearly transferred between players. The importance of these side payments is that they simplify the description of the game enormously. Instead of considering all the possible results attainable by a coalition S, we need give only the total amount which S can obtain, and point out that this can be distributed among its members in any way at all. Now, where side payments are not allowed, the form of the characteristic function becomes that much more complicated.

In general, then, the characteristic function will be a set-valued function defined on the subsets of N. First we let u_i^* be the largest utility which player i can guarantee himself, even against all the other players. Then $v(N)$, instead of being a number, is the set of all imputations: i.e., the set of all the n-vectors $(x_1, \ldots, x_n)$ which the set N, acting together, can attain.

Effectively, then, the set $v(S)$ will consist of all those vectors, x, for which the coalition S is able to guarantee its members at least their individual shares of x. (For example, the set $v(\{i\})$ will then consist of all those vectors, x, such that $x_i \leq u_i^*$.) Because of the possibility of lotteries, it is clear that each of the sets $v(S)$ is convex; it is not obvious that these sets must be closed, but we shall also make this assumption, which is not unreasonable.

X.2.1 Definition. By an n-person game without side payments we mean a pair (v, H), where H is a compact convex subset of R^n, and v is a function which assigns, to each subset S of $N = \{1, \ldots, n\}$, a subset of R^n, satisfying:

(i) $v(S)$ is closed and convex.

(ii) If $x \in v(S)$, and $y_i \leq x_i$ for all $i \in S$, then $y \in v(S)$.

(iii) If $S \cap T = \varnothing$, then $v(S) \cap v(T) \subset v(S \cup T)$.

(iv) $v(S) \neq \varnothing$ for all $S \subset N$.

(v) $x \in v(N)$ if and only if $x \leq y$ for some $y \in H$.

In this definition, condition (ii) is a monotonicity condition: if S can guarantee its members x, then it can certainly guarantee them the smaller amount y. Condition (iii) is the super-additivity condition in a new setting. Condition (v) guarantees that the set $v(N)$ is not too large; this, together with condition (iii) (letting $T = N - S$), will guarantee that the set $v(S)$ is not too large.

With this definition of imputations and characteristic function, it is possible to define the domination relation. Thus, $x \succ y$ if there is a non-empty coalition, S, such that $x_i > y_i$ for $i \in S$, and $x \in v(S)$. Stable sets and the core are then defined, exactly as in the side-payments case.

Some work has been done on stable sets of games without side payments. It has been shown by Stearns [X.14] that all three-person games will have at least one stable set; these sets have, moreover, been catalogued. However, the question of the existence of stable sets for all games has been resolved: Stearns [X.15] gives an example of a seven-person game which has no stable sets.

Some work has also been done on the core of games without side payments. Essentially, a vector $x \in v(N)$ belongs to the core if, for every coalition S and every $y \in v(S)$, there is some $i \in S$ such that $x_i \geq y_i$.

It is also possible to treat such games from the point of view of the normal form, rather than the characteristic function. When dealing with non-cooperative games, we defined an equilibrium point as an n-tuple of strategy vectors such that no player could gain by a unilateral change of strategy. We can now define a *strong equilibrium point* as an n-tuple of strategies (which can be correlated, if desired) such that there is no coalition S which can obtain an increase in utility for all its numbers if the remaining players keep to their original strategies. This definition, however, is too strong; most games will have no such points. Aumann [X.1] deals with these games by assuming that they will be played repeatedly an indefinite number of times. This gives a "supergame"; strategies for the supergame are then used in which, generally, the actual move at each replay of the original game will depend on the outcomes of the previous games. Strong equilibrium points are then defined *for the supergame* as just described. Unfortunately, many games have no strong equilibrium points even in this weaker sense.

Finally, a value concept has been defined for these games. There are several suggested schemes:

Shapley [X.13] obtains the Shapley value by assuming that side payments can be made. Then, if the resulting value can be obtained without the use of side payments, he suggests that this should be the value. For other games, the value is extended by requiring that it be invariant under linear transformations of any one player's utility function. This is sufficient to determine a value for every game.

Harsanyi [X.4, X.5] gives two bargaining models (one a modification of the other) based on a generalization of Nash's axioms for two-person cooperative games.

Isbell [X.6] assumes that each player's utility space is bounded (of the form [0, 1]). He uses a bargaining scheme which preserves ratios of utilities.

Miyasawa [X.10] also gives a generalization of Nash's model.

Selten [X.12] has studied several value schemes from an axiomatic point of view.

X.3 GAMES IN PARTITION FUNCTION FORM

One of the assumptions first made in our definition of the von Neumann-Morgenstern characteristic function is that, when a coalition S is formed, we must consider the worst that can happen to it. Thus we consider the possibility that the complementary coalition, $N - S$, will form. While this is reasonable from a min-max point of view, it is nevertheless clear that in many cases the coalition $N - S$ will not form, due to difficulty in communications, personal dislikes between the players, lack of incentive, or many other reasons. Assuming, then, that $N - S$ does not form, what will happen? It is clear that the amount S can obtain will depend on the particular coalition structure that forms. Thus, in a voting game, a coalition with less than an absolute majority of the votes will win because its opponents cannot agree and some might not vote at all. This gives us the idea of *partition function form.*

X.3.1 Definition. A game in *partition function form* is a function, v, which assigns to each partition $\mathcal{P} = (P_1, \ldots, P_k)$ of N a k-vector, $v^{\mathcal{P}} = (v^{\mathcal{P}}(P_1), v^{\mathcal{P}}(P_2), \ldots, v^{\mathcal{P}}(P_k))$.

Thus the partition function gives the amount that each coalition in $\mathcal{P}$ will receive, assuming that the partition (coalition structure) $\mathcal{P}$ is obtained. As in the von Neumann-Morgenstern theory, however, we are interested in the maximum that a coalition, S, can guarantee itself, whatever the other players do. This is given by

10.3.1 $$u(S) = \min_{S \in P} v^{\mathcal{P}}(S).$$

It should be noted that the set function u is not necessarily superadditive. This is explained by saying that in certain cases, coalitions between antagonistic groups could actually weaken the groups.

The idea of an imputation has to be modified. We have

X.3.2 Definition. An imputation for the n-person game in partition function form, v, is an n-vector $x = (x_1, \ldots, x_n)$ satisfying

(i) $x_i \geq u(\{i\})$

(ii) $\sum_{i=1}^{n} x_i = \sum_{S \in \mathcal{P}} v^{\mathcal{P}}(S)$ for some $\mathcal{P}$

Thus, the components of an imputation do not always have the same sum for these games. The idea of domination is also somewhat different.

X.3.3 Definition. An imputation x is said to dominate y through the coalition S (notation: $x \succ_S y$) if:

(i) $x_i > y_i$ for $i \in S$

(ii) $\sum_{i \in S} x_i \leq u(S)$

(iii) There is some $\mathscr{P}$ such that $S \in \mathscr{P}$ and

$$\sum_{i=1}^{n} x_i = \sum_{T \in \mathscr{P}} v^{\mathscr{P}}(T).$$

The first two conditions are the same as before; the third one, which is new, is called realizability.

We might say that, in the general case, each partition, $\mathscr{P}$, will give a different value for the sum

$$\sum_{S \in \mathscr{P}} v^{\mathscr{P}}(S) = \|\mathscr{P}\|.$$

The von Neumann-Morgenstern games, then, can be thought of as degenerate special cases in which, whatever coalition structures form, the sum of the utilities received by the players is always the same. Now, we have noted that the von Neumann-Morgenstern games quite often have enormous numbers of stable set solutions. It turns out that this multiplicity of stable sets is precisely due to the degeneracy of the characteristic function.

We have, indeed, the following theorem:

X.3.4 Theorem. If v is a four-person game such that the numbers $\|\mathscr{P}\|$ are different for all partitions, then v has a unique stable set.

We shall prove this theorem farther on. We must, however, first lay the groundwork for the proof. We shall say that a coalition S is *effective* for an imputation x if

$$\sum_{i \in S} x_i \leq u(S)$$

and *strictly effective* if

$$\sum_{i \in S} x_i < u(S).$$

X.3.5 Lemma. No imputation x can dominate another, y, through a one-player coalition $\{i\}$.

PROOF: If $x \succ_{\{i\}} y$, then we must have $y_i < x_i \leq u(\{i\})$. But this means y is not an imputation.

X.3.6 Lemma. If $x \succ_S y$, and $y_i \geq z_i$ for all $i \in S$, then $x \succ_S z$.

PROOF: Obvious.

X.3.7 Lemma. In a four-person game where the numbers $\|\mathscr{P}\|$ are all distinct, given any imputation x, there is at most one coalition which is strictly effective for x and can realize x.

PROOF: Since the numbers $\|\mathscr{P}\|$ are distinct, there is only one partition $\mathscr{P}$ which can realize x. Hence x is realizable only for the coalitions in this partition. But a one-person coalition cannot be strictly effective for an imputation, and the only partitions with more than one coalition of more than one element are of the form $\{\{i, j\}, \{k, l\}\}$. Suppose that $\mathscr{P}$ is of this form, and assume $\{i, j\}$ is strictly effective for x. Then we have

$$v^{\mathscr{P}}(\{i, j\}) \geq u(\{i, j\}) > x_i + x_j.$$

But, as x is realized by $\mathscr{P}$, we have also

$$x_i + x_j + x_k + x_l = \|\mathscr{P}\| = v^{\mathscr{P}}(\{i, j\}) + v(\{k, l\})$$

and so

$$x_k + x_l > v^{\mathscr{P}}(\{k, l\}) \geq u(\{k, l\}).$$

Thus $\{k, l\}$ is *not* effective for x.

We proceed now to prove X.3.4. A four-person game has 15 partitions; we number them $\mathscr{P}_1, \mathscr{P}_2, \ldots, \mathscr{P}_{15}$, in order of decreasing norm:

$$\|\mathscr{P}_j\| > \|\mathscr{P}_{j+1}\| \quad \text{for } j = 1, \ldots, 14.$$

We let E_j be the set of all imputations x such that $\sum x_i = \|\mathscr{P}_j\|$; this gives us $E = \bigcup_{j=1}^{15} E_j$. We next introduce the restricted cores

$$C_j = \left\{x \in E \,\middle|\, \sum_{i \in M} x_i \geq u(M) \quad \text{for all } M \in \bigcup_{k=1}^{j} \mathscr{P}_k\right\}$$

for $j = 1, \ldots, 15$, and set $C_0 = E$. It is easily seen that $C_j \subset C_{j-1}$. Let m be the smallest integer j such that $C_j \cap E_{j+1} = \varnothing$. If $C_j \cap A_{j+1} \neq \varnothing$ for $j = 1, \ldots, 14$, let $m = 15$. Note $m > 0$ as $C_0 \cap E = E_1 \neq \varnothing$. Finally, we define

$$Q = \bigcup_{j=1}^{m} (E_j \cap C_{j-1})$$

X.3.8 Lemma. Let R be a subset of Q such that each $x \in Q - R$ is dominated by some $y \in R$. Then each $x \in E - R$ is dominated by some $y \in R$.

PROOF: If $x \in E - Q$, then $x \in E_t$ for some t, and there is some $M \in \mathscr{P}_j$, with $j \leq \min(m, t-1)$, which is strictly effective for x. Choose $M_0 \in \mathscr{P}_s$ so as to make s minimal: i.e., so that $M_0 \in \mathscr{P}_s$ is strictly effective for x, but if $M \in \mathscr{P}_j$, with $j \leq s-1$, M is not strictly effective for x. Choose $z \in E_s$ so that M_0 is effective for z, and $z_i > x_i$ for all $i \in N$. Then $z \in E_s \cap C_{s-1} \subset Q$. If $z \in R$, then $z \succ x$ through M_0, and z is the desired y. If $z \notin R$, then some $y \in R$ dominates z, and, by Lemma X.3.6, $y \succ x$. Hence, in either case, x is dominated by some $y \in R$.

X.3.9 Lemma. If R is a stable set, then $R \subset Q$.

PROOF: Let $x \in E - Q$. As in Lemma X.3.8, there is some $z \in Q$ such that $z \succ x$, and, if $y \succ z$, we must have $y \succ x$. Then, if $z \in R$, we cannot have $x \in R$. If $z \notin R$, then there is $y \in R$ such that $y \succ z$. But then $y \succ x$, and so $x \notin R$.

X.3.10 Proof of X.3.4: In view of the previous lemmata, it is sufficient to show that Q contains a unique stable set. We shall do this by constructing a subset $R_j \subset E_j \cap C_{j-1}$ for $j = 1, \ldots, m$, and showing that $\bigcup_{j=1}^{m} R_j = R$ is a stable set.

First, let K_m contain all those elements of $E_m \cap C_{m-1}$ which are maximal with respect to the relation $\succ$. Since $\succ_M$ is a partial ordering, and because $E_m \cap C_{m-1}$ is a compact set, it will follow by Zorn's lemma that, given any $x \in E_m \cap C_{m-1}$ which is not maximal with respect to $\succ_M$, there will be some y which is maximal with respect to this relation, and such that $y \succ_M x$. Now, this means that M is effective for y, and strictly effective for x. Hence $M \in \mathscr{P}_m$ as $x \in C_{m-1}$, and so y is realizable for M.

Now, there is no $z \in E_m \cap C_{m-1}$ such that $z \succ y$. For, suppose $z \succ y$ through S. This means S is strictly effective for y, and that z, and hence y, are realizable for y. But $S \neq M$, and so by Lemma X.3.7, M cannot be effective for y. Hence y is maximal in $E_m \cap C_{m-1}$ for the relation $\succ$, and so $y \in R_m = K_m$. We see, hence, that any $x \in E_m \cap C_{m-1} - R_m$ is dominated by some $y \in R_m$. Moreover, by maximality under $\succ$, it follows that no $x \in R_m$ dominates any $y \in R_m$.

We proceed to construct sets $K_{m-1}, K_{m-2}, \ldots, K_1$ as follows: Suppose we have constructed $K_m, K_{m-1}, \ldots, K_{j+1}$. Let $R_{j+1} = \bigcup_{j+1}^{m} K_l$. Now, let G_j be that subset of $E_j \cap C_{j-1}$ consisting of imputations which are not dominated by any elements of R_{j+1}. Let K_j be the subset of G_j consisting of elements which are maximal (in G_j) under the relation $\succ$. Again, we note that G_j is compact, and so it follows that every $x \in G_j - K_j$ is dominated by some $y \in K_j$, and so every $x \in E_j \cap C_{j-1} - K_j$ is dominated by some $y \in R_j = \bigcup_j^m K_l$.

Assume now (as an induction hypothesis) that no element of R_{j+1} dominates another element of R_{j+1}, and that if

$$x \in \bigcup_{j+1}^{m} (E_l \cap C_{l-1}) - R_{j+1},$$

there is some $y \in R_{j+1}$ such that $y \succ x$. Suppose that both x and y are in R_j. As $R_j = R_{j+1} \cup K_j$, there are four possibilities:

$$\begin{array}{lll} \text{(i)} & x \in R_{j+1}, & y \in R_{j+1} \\ \text{(ii)} & x \in R_{j+1}, & y \in K_j \\ \text{(iii)} & x \in K_j, & y \in R_{j+1} \\ \text{(iv)} & x \in K_j, & y \in K_j. \end{array}$$

In case (i), by the induction hypothesis, we cannot have $x \succ y$. In case (ii), we cannot have $x \succ y$ as $y \in G_j$ and $x \in R_{j+1}$. In case (iii), we cannot have $x \succ y$, as this would mean that some $M \in P_j$ was strictly effective for y. But $y \in C_j$, so this is not possible. Finally, in case (iv), we cannot have $x \succ y$ since both x and y are maximal in G_j under the relation $\succ$. Thus, if x and y are both in R_j, we cannot have $x \succ y$.

Suppose, on the other hand, that $x \in \bigcup_j^m (E_l \cap C_{l-1}) - R_j$. Then either

$$\text{(i)} \quad x \in \bigcup_{j+1}^{m} (E_l \cap C_{l-1}) - R_{j+1}$$

or

$$\text{(ii)} \quad x \in E_j \cap C_{j-1} - K_j.$$

In case (i), by the induction hypothesis, there is $y \in R_{j+1}$ such that $y \succ x$. In case (ii), we saw above that there is $y \in K_j$ such that $y \succ x$. In either case, there is some $y \in R_j$ such that $y \succ x$.

When we proceed in this manner, we arrive at a set $R = R_1$ which satisfies the hypothesis of X.3.8 and is obviously internally stable. Thus R will be a stable set.

We must now show that R is the unique stable set. This is not too difficult to do, and will, in fact, be left as a problem (X.3).

The proof of Theorem X.3.4 uses Zorn's lemma, but in such a weak manner that it is practically a constructive proof. We give an example below of the way in which it may be used to find a stable set. Because of the large number of imputation simplices, however, we shall consider only a three-person game. Now, while a four-person game has 15 partitions, a three-person game has only five partitions. Hence the three-person game is that much simpler. It may be seen that Theorem X.3.4 applies also to three-person games.

X.3.11 Example. Consider a three-person game with $\mathscr{P}_1 = \{\{1, 2\}, \{3\}\}$, $\mathscr{P}_2 = \{\{1, 3\}, \{2\}\}$, $\mathscr{P}_3 = \{\{1\}, \{2, 3\}\}$, $\mathscr{P}_4 = \{\{1, 2, 3\}\}$, $\mathscr{P}_5 = \{\{1\}, \{2\}, \{3\}\}$, and

$$\begin{aligned} v^{\mathscr{P}_1}(\{1, 2\}) &= 5 \\ v^{\mathscr{P}_1}(\{3\}) &= 5 \\ v^{\mathscr{P}_2}(\{1, 3\}) &= 5 \\ v^{\mathscr{P}_2}(\{2\}) &= 3 \\ v^{\mathscr{P}_3}(\{2, 3\}) &= 6 \\ v^{\mathscr{P}_3}(\{1\}) &= 0 \\ v^{\mathscr{P}_4}(\{1, 2, 3\}) &= 4 \\ v^{\mathscr{P}_5}(\{i\}) &= 0 \quad \text{for } i = 1, 2, 3. \end{aligned}$$

This gives $\|\mathscr{P}_1\| = 10$, $\|\mathscr{P}_2\| = 8$, $\|\mathscr{P}_3\| = 6$, $\|\mathscr{P}_4\| = 4$, $\|\mathscr{P}_5\| = 0$, and $u(\{1, 2\}) = u(\{1, 3\}) = 5$, $u(\{2, 3\}) = 6$, $u(\{i\}) = 0$. It is easy to see that $E_3 \cap C_2 \neq \varnothing$, while $E_4 \cap C_3 = \varnothing$, so that $m = 3$. We construct R as follows.

First, note that E_3 is the simplex of non-negative vectors with sum 6; $E_3 \cap C_2$ will consist of those elements of E_3 which satisfy

$$\begin{aligned} x_1 + x_2 &\geq 5 \\ x_1 + x_3 &\geq 5 \end{aligned}$$

or, equivalently,

$$\begin{aligned} x_2 &\leq 1 \\ x_3 &\leq 1. \end{aligned}$$

Now, domination in E_3 can only be through $\{2, 3\}$. Hence K_3 consists of those elements of $E_3 \cap C_2$ which are maximal with respect to $\succ$ through $\{2, 3\}$. Now, if $x_2 < 1$ and $x_3 < 1$, then $y \succ x$, where $y = (4, 1, 1)$. On the other hand, if $x_2 = 1$, or $x_3 = 1$, then x cannot be dominated in $E_3 \cap C_2$. Thus K_3 is given by the union of the two segments

10.3.2 $\quad x_2 = 1, \quad 0 \leq x_3 \leq 1$

and

10.3.3 $\quad x_3 = 1, \quad 0 \leq x_2 \leq 1.$

Consider now $E_2 \cap C_1$. E_2 consists of non-negative vectors with sum 8; $E_2 \cap C_1$ consists of those elements of E_2 which also satisfy $x_1 + x_2 \geq 5$, or, equivalently, $x_3 \leq 3$. To obtain G_2, we must delete those elements of $E_2 \cap C_1$ which are dominated by K_3. Now, the only coalition which can realize imputations in K_3 is $\{2, 3\}$; from the form of K_3, it follows that we must delete those elements of $E_2 \cap C_1$ for which $x_2 < 1$ and $x_3 < 1$. Thus G_2 is given by:

$$x_1 + x_2 + x_3 = 8$$
$$x_3 \leq 3$$
$$x_2 \geq 1 \quad \textit{or} \quad x_3 \geq 1.$$

Now, we want those elements in G_2 which are maximal with respect to $\succ$. As $\{1, 3\}$ is the realizing coalition, any x such that $x_1 + x_3 < 5$, $x_3 < 3$ will be dominated by some $y \in G_2$. It is then easy to show that K_2 consists of the union of the three sets

10.3.4 $\quad 0 \leq x_2 \leq 1, \quad 1 \leq x_3 \leq 3$

10.3.5 $\quad 1 \leq x_2 \leq 3, \quad 0 \leq x_3 \leq 3$

and

10.3.6 $\quad x_3 = 3.$

Consider now $E_1 \cap C_0 = E_1$. This consists of all non-negative vectors whose sum is 10. To obtain G_1, we must remove all imputations in E_1 dominated by $R_2 = K_2 \cup K_3$. Now, the imputations dominated by K_3 are those which have $x_2 < 1$, $x_3 < 1$. The imputations dominated by K_2 are those which have $x_1 + x_3 < 5$, $x_3 < 3$. Thus G_1 is given by

$$x_2 \geq 1 \quad \text{or} \quad x_3 \geq 1$$
$$x_2 \leq 5 \quad \text{or} \quad x_3 \geq 3.$$

Now, it may be seen that G_1 contains all imputations in E, for which $x_3 = 5$. Hence, if $y_3 < 5$, it will be dominated through

{1, 2} by some $x \in G_1$. All other elements of G_1 will belong to K_1, which is therefore given as the union of the sets.

10.3.7 $0 \leq x_2 \leq 1, \qquad 1 \leq x_3 \leq 5$

and

10.3.8 $1 \leq x_2 \leq 5, \qquad 0 \leq x_3 \leq 5$

and

10.3.9 $x_2 \geq 5, \qquad x_3 \geq 3.$

The conditions (10.3.2)–(10.3.9) will give the three sets K_1, K_2, K_3. The set $R = K_1 \cup K_2 \cup K_3$ is the unique stable set solution of our given game. (See Figure X.3.1.)

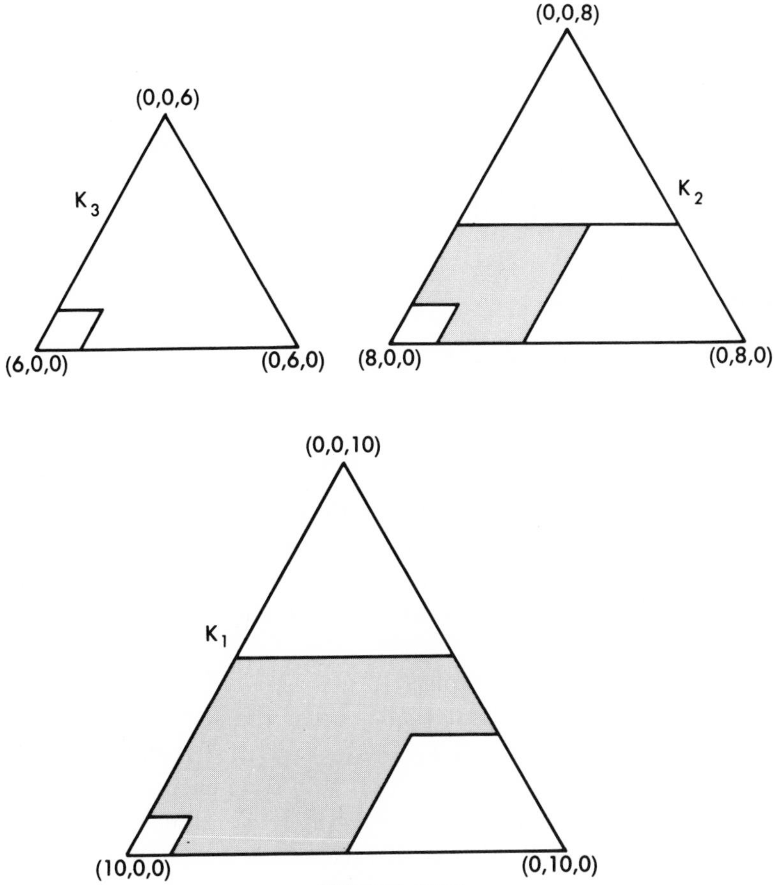

FIGURE X.3.1

PROBLEMS

1. The sum of any number of measures is also a measure. Show that, if $P(\mu_1, \ldots, \mu_m)$ is a polynomial in the measures μ_i, then P can be written in the form $P = c_1\nu_1^{n_1} + c_2\nu_2^{n_2} + \cdots + c_k\nu_k^{n_k}$ where the c_j are constants, the ν_j are measures, and the n_j are positive integers.

2. For $S \subset [0, 1]$, let $v(S) = \lambda^3(S)\mu(S)$ where λ is Lebesgue measure and $\mu(S) = \int_S x\,dx$. Find the Shapley value $\varphi[v]$ of this game.

3. Complete the proof of X.3.4 (i.e., show that the R constructed in this proof is the only stable set). Do this by showing, inductively, that $K_m, K_{m-1}, \ldots, K_1$ must all be subsets of any stable set.

4. An n-person game without side payments need not have a stable set. Consider the simple seven-player game v, where H is the convex hull of the five points

$$c = (2, 0, 2, 0, 2, 0, 1)$$
$$p_1 = (1, 1, 2, 0, 0, 0, 0)$$
$$p_2 = (0, 0, 1, 1, 2, 0, 0)$$
$$p_3 = (2, 0, 0, 0, 1, 1, 0)$$
$$0 = (0, 0, 0, 0, 0, 0, 0)$$

and the minimal winning coalitions are $\{1, 3, 5\}$, $\{1, 2, 7\}$, $\{3, 4, 7\}$, $\{5, 6, 7\}$. Any winning coalition can enforce any imputation, whereas the other coalitions are effective only for the imputations in which their members receive 0. Then v has no stable set solutions.

(a) The core of v is simply $\{c\}$.

(b) If L_i is the segment $[p_i, c]$, then the set of imputations undominated by c is $L_1 \cup L_2 \cup L_3$. If V is stable it must contain at least one point, $q_i \neq c$, from each L_i.

(c) The points q_i must satisfy $q_1^7 = q_2^7 = q_3^7$. Hence V contains only one point other than c from each L_i. Hence V is not stable; v has no stable set solutions.

APPENDIX

A.1 CONVEXITY

Throughout this book, the notion of convexity has been used extensively. We give below some of the properties of convex functions, though other properties have been given in the text, notably in Chapters II and IV.

A.1.1 Definition. A real-valued function $f(x)$, defined over a real linear space, is said to be *convex* iff, for any values x, y of the independent variable, and any r such that $0 \leq r \leq 1$,

1.1 $$f(rx + (1 - r)y) \leq rf(x) + (1 - r)f(y).$$

The function f is said to be *strictly convex* if, whenever $x \neq y$ and $0 < r < 1$, strict inequality holds in Equation 1.1.

A.1.2 Definition. A function f is said to be concave (strictly concave) iff $-f$ is convex (strictly convex).

The following theorem gives obvious properties of convex functions. No proof is given.

A.1.3 Theorem. Let f and g be convex functions, and suppose that $c \geq 0$. Then the functions $f + g$, cf, and max $\{f, g\}$ are all convex.

In a similar way, if f and g are concave, so are $f + g$, cf, and min $\{f, g\}$.

It is easy to see that a linear function is both concave and convex. Conversely, if a function is both concave and convex, it is linear.

A.1.4 Definition. A set $S \subset V$, where V is a real linear space, is said to be *convex*, iff whenever $x, y \in S$ and $0 \leq r \leq 1$, then

1.2 $rx + (1 - r)y \in S$.

Thus, a set S is convex if the segment joining two points in S lies entirely in S. This compares with the idea that a function is convex if the chord joining two points on the graph of the function lies entirely above the surface. Thus, the set of points *above* the graph of a convex function is convex (this is often given as the definition of a convex function). This relation between convex sets and convex functions is mirrored in the following theorem, which represents a partial analogue of A.1.3. Its proof is trivial.

A.1.5 Theorem. Let S_α be convex for $\alpha \in A$ (where A is some index set). Then $\bigcap_{\alpha \in A} S_\alpha$ is also convex.

Very often we are given a non-convex set K, and we wish to apply some theorem which holds only for convex sets. This makes it necessary for us to associate with K a convex set, $H(K)$.

A.1.6 Definition. Let K be any set. Then its *convex hull*, $H(K)$, is the intersection of all the convex sets which contain K.

By Theorem A.1.5, the convex hull of any set is convex; it is clear that, if a set is convex, it is its own convex hull. There is, however, a different way of defining the convex hull: i.e., in terms of *convex linear combinations*.

A.1.7 Definition. Let $x^1, x^2, \ldots, x^p$ be p points in some real linear space. The point y will then be said to be a *convex linear combination* of $x^1, x^2, \ldots, x^p$ if there exist real numbers, $c_1, \ldots, c_p$, satisfying:

(i) $c_j \geq 0 \qquad j = 1, \ldots, p$

(ii) $\sum c_j = 1$

(iii) $y = \sum c_j x^j$.

The connection between convex linear combinations and the convex hull is shown in the following theorem.

A.1.8 Theorem. For any set K, the convex hull $H(K)$ is precisely the set S of all points y which are convex linear combinations of elements of K.

PROOF: It is easy to see that $K \subset S$. Now, S is convex, for suppose

$$y = \sum_{1}^{p} c_j x^j \qquad x^1, \ldots, x^p \in K$$

and

$$y' = \sum_{p+1}^{p+q} c_j x^j \qquad x^{p+1}, \ldots, x^{p+q} \in K$$

are both in S, with $(c_1, \ldots, c_p)$ and $(c_{p+1}, \ldots, c_{p+q})$ satisfying (i) and (ii) of A.1.7 above. Then, if $0 \leq r \leq 1$, we can write

$$y'' = ry + (1 - r)y' = \sum_{j=1}^{p} (rc_j)x^j + \sum_{j=p+1}^{p+q} (1 - r)c_j x^j$$

and the numbers $(rc_1, \ldots, rc_p, (1 - r)c_{p+1}, \ldots, (1 - r)c_{p+q})$ satisfy A.1.7 (i), (ii). Hence, $y'' \in S$, and so S is convex. It follows that $H(K) \subset S$.

Conversely, let $y = \sum_{j=1}^{p} c_j x^j$, where $x^j \in K$, and the c_j are as above. We prove by induction on p that $y \in H(K)$. In fact, for $p = 1, y = x^1$ and so $y \in K \subset H(K)$. Suppose, then, that this is true for $p - 1$. We may assume, without loss of generality, that $c_1 > 0$, and so $r = \sum_{j=1}^{p-1} c_j > 0$. We have then

$$y = ry' + (1 - r)x^p$$

where

$$y' = \sum_{j=1}^{p-1} \frac{c_j}{r} x^j.$$

It is clear that $y' \in S$ and so, by the induction hypothesis, $y' \in H(K)$. But $x^p \in H(K)$. By convexity, it follows that $y \in H(K)$. Hence, $S \subset H(K)$. This proves the theorem.

The idea of a convex hull enables us to assign a convex set to any set. On the other hand, it is sometimes of interest to reduce a convex set to some subset, whose convex hull it is.

A.1.9 Definition. Let S be a convex set, and suppose that $x \in S$. We say that x is an *extreme point* of S if there do *not* exist two points, x', x'' in S, such that $x' \neq x''$ and

$$x = \tfrac{1}{2}(x' + x'').$$

The following theorem is of importance and has been used in the text of this book.

A.1.10 Theorem. A compact convex subset S of n-dimensional Euclidean space is the convex hull of its extreme points. Moreover, any $y \in S$ can be expressed as a convex linear combination of at most $n + 1$ extreme points of S.

PROOF: It is clear that the second part of the theorem implies the first. We shall, therefore, prove only this second part. We prove it by induction on n. In fact, for $n = 1$, the only compact convex sets are the empty set $\varnothing$, single points, and intervals $[a, b]$. For $\varnothing$ and single points, the theorem is trivial; for sets $[a, b]$, it is clear that a and b are extreme, and every $y \in [a, b]$ is a convex linear combination of a and b.

Assume, then, that the theorem is true for $n - 1$. It is clear that it will hold for all $(n - 1)$-dimensional sets, even when these are subsets of a higher-dimensional space. Let S be as in the hypothesis, and let $y \in S$.

Take any line passing through y. Because of compactness and convexity, the intersection of this line and S is a closed line-segment, with end-points y' and y''.

Consider the point y'. It is a boundary point of S, and hence (see Problem II.1), there is a hyperplane, P, passing through y' such that the set S lies entirely on or "above" (to one side of) P. Clearly, P is closed and convex, and hence $S \cap P$ is a compact convex set of dimension at most $n - 1$. As $y' \in S \cap P$, it can be expressed as a linear combination of at most n extreme points of $S \cap P$.

Suppose that $x \in S \cap P$, and suppose that $x = \tfrac{1}{2}(x' + x'')$, with $x', x'' \in S$. The set P can be characterized by an equation $L(x) = \alpha$, where L is a linear functional, and we know $L(x) \geq \alpha$ for all $x \in S$. By linearity, we must have $L(x') = L(x'') = \alpha$, and so $x', x'' \in P$. This means that, if x is extreme in $S \cap P$, it is extreme in P.

We have thus shown that y is a convex linear combination

of the point y'' and at most n extreme points of S. However, y'' was obtained by taking an arbitrary line through y; this line can always be taken so that y'' is extreme. Thus y will be a linear combination of at most $n + 1$ extreme points of S.

A.2 FIXED POINT THEOREMS

We give below, without proof, two theorems which have been used in the text. The proofs of these theorems are quite lengthy and can be found in the references in the Bibliography.

A.2.1 Theorem (The Brouwer fixed point theorem). Let S be a compact convex subset of n-dimensional Euclidean space, and let f be a continuous function mapping S into itself. Then there exists at least one $x \in S$ such that $f(x) = x$.

This theorem is a topological theorem and thus will apply to any set topologically equivalent to such a set S. (Quite often, it is stated that S is an n-simplex.) The proof in the general case is quite lengthy and requires an extensive background in topology, though for $n = 1$, it is an easy consequence of the intermediate value theorem (it then reduces to showing that the equation $f(x) - x = 0$ has a root in the given interval). A generalization which is very useful in game theory is the Kakutani fixed point theorem, given below.

A.2.2 Definition. Let f be a function with domain X (a topological space) and such that, for $x \in X$, $f(x)$ is a subset of some topological space Y. Then, f is said to be *upper semi-continuous* (u.s.c.) at a point x_0 if for any sequence $x_1, x_2, \ldots,$ converging to x_0, and any sequence of points $y_1, y_2, \ldots$ with $y_i \in f(x_i)$, the limit of the sequence $\{y_n\}$ (if the sequence converges) belongs to $f(x_0)$. The function f is upper semi-continuous if it is u.s.c. at each point of X.

A.2.3 Theorem (Kakutani). Let S be a compact convex subset of n-dimensional Euclidean space, and let f be an upper semi-continuous function which assigns to each $x \in S$ a closed convex subset of S. Then there is some $x \in S$ such that $x \in f(x)$.

BIBLIOGRAPHY

General. The following books contain material of general interest, as opposed to books and papers which are more properly related to one or another chapter of this work and which are given in chapter bibliographies.

1. Dresher, M., L. S. Shapley, and A. W. Tucker, eds., *Advances in Game Theory*, Annals of Mathematics Studies No. 52, Princeton (Princeton University Press), 1964.
2. Dresher, M., A. W. Tucker, and P. Wolfe, eds., *Contributions to the Theory of Games, III*, Annals of Mathematics Studies No. 39, Princeton (Princeton University Press), 1957.
3. Karlin, S., *Mathematical Methods and Theory in Games, Programming and Economics*, Reading, Mass. (Addison-Wesley Publishing Co., Inc.), 1959.
4. Kuhn, H. W., and A. W. Tucker, eds., *Contributions to the Theory of Games, I–II*, Annals of Mathematics Studies Nos. 24, 28, Princeton (Princeton University Press), 1950, 1953.
5. Kuhn, H. W., and A. W. Tucker, eds., *Linear Inequalities and Related Systems*, Annals of Mathematics Studies No. 38, Princeton (Princeton University Press), 1956.
6. Luce, R. D., and H. Raiffa, *Games and Decisions*, New York (John Wiley and Sons, Inc.), 1957.
7. Tucker, A. W., and R. D. Luce, eds., *Contributions to the Theory of Games, IV*, Annals of Mathematics Studies No. 40. Princeton (Princeton University Press), 1959.
8. von Neumann, J., and O. Morgenstern, *Theory of Games and Economic Behavior*. Princeton (Princeton University Press), 1944, 1947.

References 1, 2, 4, 5, and 7 above consist of many separate papers and will be referred to, in the chapter bibliographies, as *Annals 24*, *Annals 28*, etc.

CHAPTER I

1. Berge, C., "Topological Games with Perfect Information," *Annals 39.*
2. Gale, D., and F. M. Stewart, "Infinite Games with Perfect Information," *Annals 28.*
3. Kuhn, H. W., "A Simplified Two-Person Poker," *Annals 24.*
4. Kuhn, H. W., "Extensive Games and the Problem of Information," *Annals 28.*
5. Nash, J., and L. S. Shapley, "A Simple Three-Person Poker Game," *Annals 24.*

CHAPTER II

1. Brown, G. W., and J. von Neumann, "Solutions of Games by Differential Equations," *Annals 24.*
2. Dresher, M., and S. Karlin, "Solutions of Convex Games as Fixed Points," *Annals 28.*
3. Farkas, J., "Theorie der Einfachen Ungleichungen," *J. Reine Angew. Math.* 124 (1902), pp. 1–27.
4. Gale, D., H. W. Kuhn, and A. W. Tucker, "On Symmetric Games," *Annals 24.*
5. Motzkin, T. S., H. Raiffa, G. L. Thompson, and R. M. Thrall, "The Double Description Method," *Annals 28.*
6. Robinson, J., "An Iterative Method of Solving a Game," *Annals of Mathematics* 54 (1951), pp. 296–301.
7. Shapley, L. S., and R. N. Snow, "Basic Solutions of Discrete Games," *Annals 24.*
8. Weyl, H., "Elementary Proof of a Minimax Theorem due to von Neumann," *Annals 24.*

CHAPTER III

1. Dantzig, G., L. R. Ford, and D. R. Fulkerson, "A Primal-Dual Algorithm for Linear Programs," *Annals 38.*
2. Dantzig, G., and D. R. Fulkerson, "On the Max-Flow Min-Cut Theorem of Networks," *Annals 38.*
3. Gass, S. I., *Linear Programming*, New York (McGraw-Hill Book Co.), 1958.
4. Goldman, A., and A. W. Tucker, "Theory of Linear Programming," *Annals 38.*
5. Tucker, A. W., "Dual Systems of Homogeneous Linear Relations," *Annals 38.*
6. Vajda, S., *The Theory of Games and Linear Programming*, London (Methuen & Co., Ltd.), New York (John Wiley and Sons, Inc.), 1956.
7. Wolfe, P., "Determinateness of Polyhedral Games," *Annals 38.*

CHAPTER IV

1. Bohnenblust, H. F., S. Karlin, and L. S. Shapley, "Games with Continuous Convex Payoff," *Annals 24.*
2. Bohnenblust, H. F., S. Karlin, and L. S. Shapley, "Solutions of Discrete Two-Person Games," *Annals 24.*
3. Borel, E., "Sur les jeux où interviennent le hasard et l'habileté des joueurs," *Eléments de la Théorie des Probabilités,* 3ème edition, Paris (Librairie Scientifique), 1924.
4. Dresher, M., S. Karlin, and L. S. Shapley, "Polynomial Games," *Annals 24.*
5. Duffin, R. J., "Infinite Programs," *Annals 38.*
6. Gross, O., "A Rational Game on the Square," *Annals 39.*
7. Karlin, S., "Operator Treatment of the Minmax Principle," *Annals 24.*
8. Karlin, S., "On a Class of Games," *Annals 28.*
9. Karlin, S., "Reduction of Certain Classes of Games to Integral Equations," *Annals 28.*
10. Restrepo, R., "Tactical Problems Involving Several Actions," *Annals 39.*
11. Shiffman, M., "Games of Timing," *Annals 28.*
12. Sion, M., and P. Wolfe, "On a Game Without a Value," *Annals 39.*

CHAPTER V

1. Berkovitz, L. D., and W. H. Fleming, "On Differential Games with Integral Payoff," *Annals 39.*
2. Berkovitz, L. D., "A Variational Approach to Differential Games," *Annals 52.*
3. Berkovitz, L. D., "A Differential Game without Pure Strategy Solutions on an Open Set," *Annals 52.*
4. Blackwell, D., "Multi-Component Attrition Games," *Naval Research Logistics Quarterly* 1 (1954), pp. 327–332.
5. Dubins, L. E., "A Discrete Evasion Game," *Annals 39.*
6. Everett, H., "Recursive Games," *Annals 39.*
7. Fleming, W. H., "The Convergence Problem for Differential Games," *Annals 52.*
8. Isaacs, R., *Differential Games*, New York (John Wiley & Sons, Inc.), 1965.
9. Isbell, J., "Finitary Games," *Annals 39.*
10. Milnor, J., and L. S. Shapley, "On Games of Survival," *Annals 39.*
11. Mycielski, J., "Continuous Games of Perfect Information," *Annals 52.*
12. Ryll-Nardzewski, C., "A Theory of Pursuit and Evasion," *Annals 52.*
13. Scarf, H. E., "On Differential Games with Survival Payoff," *Annals 39.*
14. Shapley, L. S., "Stochastic Games," *Proc. Nat. Acad. Sci. U.S.A.* 39 (1953), pp. 327–332.

CHAPTER VI

1. Arrow, K. J., *Social Choice and Individual Values*, Cowlen Commission Monograph 12, New York (John Wiley and Sons, Inc.), 1951.
2. Davidson, D., S. Siegel, and P. Suppes, "Some Experiments and Related Theory on the Measurement of Utility and Subjective Probability,"

Applied Mathematics and Statistics Laboratory, *Technical Report 1*, Stanford University, 1955.
3. Hausner, M., "Multi-Dimensional Utilities," *Decision Processes*, ed. Thrall, Coombs, and Davis, New York (John Wiley and Sons, Inc.), 1954.
4. Hernstein, J. N., and J. Milnor, "An Axiomatic Approach to Measurable Utility," *Econometrica* 21 (1953), pp. 291–297.
5. Isbell, J., "Absolute Games," *Annals 40.*
6. Luce, R. D., "*A Probabilistic Theory of Utility*," *Technical Report 14*, Behavioral Models Project, Columbia University, 1956.
7. Suppes, P., and M. Winet, "An Axiomatization of Utility Based on the Notion of Utility Differences," *Man. Sci.* 1 (1955), pp. 259–270.

CHAPTER VII

1. Braithwaite, R. B., *Theory of Games as a Tool for the Moral Philosopher*, Cambridge (Cambridge University Press), 1955.
2. Harsanyi, J. C., "Approaches to the Bargaining Problem before and after the Theory of Games: a Critical Discussion of Zeuthen's, Hick's and Nash's Theories," *Econometrica* 24 (1956), pp. 144–157.
3. Harsanyi, J. C., "A Solution for Non-Cooperative Games," *Annals 52.*
4. Lemke, C. E., "Bimatrix Equilibrium Points and Mathematical Programming," *Man. Sci.* 11 (May 1965).
5. Nash, J., "Equilibrium Points in *n*-Person Games," *Proc. Nat. Acad. Sci. U.S.A.* 36 (1950), pp. 48–49.
6. Nash, J., "The Bargaining Problem," *Econometrica* 18 (1950), pp. 155–162.
7. Nash, J., "Non-Cooperative Games," *Annals of Mathematics* 54 (1951), pp. 286–295.
8. Raiffa, H., "Arbitration Schemes for Generalized Two-Person Games," *Annals 28.*
9. Shapley, L. S., "Some Topics in Two-Person Games," *Annals 52.*
10. Zeuthen, F., *Problems of Monopoly and Economic Warfare.* London (G. Routledge and Sons), 1930.

CHAPTER VIII

1. Bott, R., "Symmetric Solutions to Majority Games," *Annals 28.*
2. Gillies, D. B., "Solutions to General Non-Zero-Sum Games," *Annals 40.*
3. Gurk, H., and J. Isbell, "Simple Solutions," *Annals 40.*
4. Kalisch, G. K., and E. D. Nering, "Countably Infinitely Many Person Games," *Annals 40.*
5. McKinsey, J. C. C., "Isomorphism of Games and Strategic Equivalence," *Annals 24.*
6. Owen, G., "Tensor Composition of Non-Negative Games," *Annals 52.*
7. Owen, G., "Discriminatory Solutions of *n*-Person Games," *Proc. Am. Math. Soc.* 17 (1966), pp. 653–657.
8. Shapley, L. S., "Quota Solutions of *n*-Person Games," *Annals 28.*
9. Shapley, L. S., "A Solution Containing an Arbitrary Closed Component," *Annals 40.*
10. Shapley, L. S., "Solutions of Compound Simple Games," *Annals 52.*
11. Shubik, M., "Edgeworth Market Games," *Annals 40.*

CHAPTER IX

1. Aumann, R. J., and M. Maschler, "The Bargaining Set for Cooperative Games," *Annals 52.*
2. Luce, R. D., "ψ-Stability: a New Equilibrium Concept for n-Person Game Theory," *Mathematical Models of Human Behavior* (Proceedings of a symposium), Stamford, Conn. (Dunlap and Associates), 1955, pp. 32–44.
3. Luce, R. D., "k-Stability of Symmetric and Quota Games," *Annals of Mathematics* 62 (1955), pp. 517–527.
4. Maschler, M., "The Inequalities that Determine the Bargaining Set $\mathscr{M}_1^{(i)}$," Research Program in Game Theory and Mathematical Economics, *Research Memorandum 17,* Hebrew University of Jerusalem, January 1966.
5. Maschler, M., and B. Peleg, "A Characterization, Existence Proof, and Dimension Bounds for the Kernel of a Game," *Pacific J. Math.* 18 (1966), pp. 289–328.
6. Milnor, J., "Reasonable Outcomes for n-Person Games," *RM-916,* RAND Corporation, 1952.
7. Peleg, B., "On the Bargaining Set $\mathscr{M}_0$ of m-Quota Games," *Annals 52.*
8. Peleg, B., "Existence Theorem for the Bargaining Set $\mathscr{M}_1^{(i)}$," *Bull. Am. Math. Soc.* 69 (1963), pp. 109–110.
9. Shapley, L. S., "A Value for n-Person Games," *Annals 28.*

CHAPTER X

1. Aumann, R. J., "Acceptable Points in General Cooperative n-Person Games," *Annals 40.*
2. Aumann, R. J., "Markets with a Continuum of Traders," *Econometrica* 32 (1964), pp. 443–476.
3. Davis, M., "Symmetric Solutions to Symmetric Games with a Continuum of Players," *Recent Advances in Game Theory,* Proceedings of a Conference at Princeton University, 1961.
4. Harsanyi, J. C., "A Bargaining Model for the Cooperative n-Person Game," *Annals 40.*
5. Harsanyi, J. C., "A Simplified Bargaining Model for the n-Person Cooperative Games," *International Economic Review* 4 (May 1963).
6. Isbell, J., "Absolute Games," *Annals 40.*
7. Kannai, Y., "Values of Games with a Continuum of Players," Research Program in Game Theory and Mathematical Economics, *Research Memorandum 11,* Hebrew University of Jerusalem, August 1964.
8. Lucas, W. F., "Solutions for Four-Person Games in Partition Function Form," J. SIAM 13 (1965), pp. 118–128.
9. Milnor, J., and L. S. Shapley, "Values of Large Games II: Oceanic Games," RM-2699, RAND Corporation, February 1961.
10. Miyasawa, K., "The n-Person Bargaining Game," *Annals 52.*
11. Nering, E. D., "Coalition Bargaining in n-Person Games," *Annals 52.*
12. Selten, R., "Valuation of n-Person Games," *Annals 52.*
13. Shapley, L. S., "A Value for n-Person Games Without Side Payments," Proceedings of a conference at Princeton University, April 1965.

14. Stearns, R. E., "Three-Person Cooperative Games Without Side Payments," *Annals 52.*

15. Stearns, R. E., "On the Axioms for a Cooperative Game Without Side Payments," *Report* 62-RL-3130E, General Electric Laboratories, Schenectady, N.Y., September 1962.

APPENDIX

1. Bonnesen, T., and W. Fenchel, "Theorie der Konvexen Körper," *Ergebnisse der Mathematik und Ihrer Grenzgebiete,* Vol. 3, No. 1 Berlin (Springer), 1934; New York (Chelsea), 1948.

2. Gale, D., "Convex Polyhedral Cones and Linear Inequalities," *Activity Analysis of Production and Allocation,* ed. T. C. Koopmans, New York (John Wiley and Sons, Inc.), 1951.

3. Kakutani, S., "A Generalization of Brouwer's Fixed Point Theorem," *Duke J. Math.* 8 (1941), pp. 457–459.

4. Weyl, A., "The Elementary Theory of Convex Polyhedra," *Annals 24.*

INDEX